STEAMING TO DJIBOUTI

My First Hitch on an Underway Replenishment Ship

Captain Sean P. Tortora

Steaming to Djibouti: My First Hitch on an Underway Replenishment Ship

Published by Red Penguin Books

Bellerose Village, New York

Library of Congress Control Number: 2020916333

ISBN

Paperback 978-1-952859-36-6

Hardcover 978-1-952859-62-5

Digital 978-1-952859-35-9

Printed in the USA

Steaming to Djibouti: My First Hitch on an Underway Replenishment Ship is a travelogue and a work of fiction. Any resemblance to actual events, names, or persons, living or dead, is entirely coincidental. Certain long-standing institutions, agencies, and public offices are mentioned, but the characters involved, incidents, and situations depicted are wholly imaginary. Finally, the views expressed are those of the fictitious characters and not those of the U.S. Merchant Marine Academy, the Maritime Administration, the Department of Transportation, or the United States Government.

Photo Credits

Front cover: USNS SUPPLY T-AO 6 conducting underway replenishment with aircraft carrier USS GEORGE WASHINGTON CVN-73, circa 2002, photo courtesy of CAPT Terry Rycenga, USMM (ret.)

Back cover: USNS SUPPLY T-AO 6 conducting underway replenishment with USS NORMANDY CG-60 circa, 2002, photo courtesy of CAPT Terry Rycenga, USMM (ret.)

For Jennifer

CONTENTS

Heave Ho! My Lads, Heave Ho!
It's a long, long way to go.
It's a long, long pull with our hatches full,
Braving the wind, braving the sea,
Fighting the treacherous foe;
Heave Ho! My lads, Heave Ho!
Let the sea roll high or low,
We can cross any ocean, sail any river.
Give us the goods and we'll deliver,
Damn the submarine!
We're the men of the Merchant Marine!

Heave Ho! My Lads! Heave Ho!
The official Song of the U.S. Merchant Marine
Words and music by
LT(jg) Jack Lawrence, USMS, circa 1943

CHAPTER ONE

"The sea is selective, slow at recognition of effort and aptitude, but fast at sinking the unfit."

- Felix Riesenberg

Superintendent

New York Nautical School

1917-1919

Standing on a pier, alone, waiting for a ship... How did I arrive here…?

I came into this world Francis Kowalski Natale born in the year of Our Lord 1967 in the hamlet of Amityville, New York on Long Island's South Shore. I was the son of a first-generation Italian-American father and a Polish-American mother. My father, a Bronx native, was a U.S. Merchant Marine engineering officer, Chief engineer at that, serving some thirty-five or so years through World War II until 1975. My mother, some fifteen years his junior, was an elementary school teacher from Long Island. Their first date was at an old Howard Johnson's diner in the Bronx in 1965. My mother brought her two little girls, and at the end of the date she dropped my father off at his ship berthed at pier 92 on the west side of Manhattan—and he was off to sea. That ship was none other than the passenger liner *SS United States.*

Before going any further, I feel it necessary to relay something of the man who inspired me to follow his footsteps and go to sea. My father, Caesar Natale, was larger than life. He was raised in the Belmont section of the Bronx, also known as the "Little Italy" of the Bronx, so as not to confuse this with Mulberry Street and Manhattan's Little Italy section. The Belmont section included what is now the iconic Arthur Avenue and the famous Arthur Avenue Market. However, back in the 1920's and 1930's, the section was also known for its wise guys. When I mean wise guys, I mean those wise guys who wear the finest sharkskin suits topped with a fedora hat walking around like they own the place...because they did. My family owned a filling station and garage. Caesar was quite handsome, having won the prestigious professional photography portrait award for the City of New York for 1937. Years later Caesar would often be confused as Clark Gable's doppelganger. After high school, my father attended the famed acting school, the American Academy of Dramatic Arts. He graduated in 1939 with future Oscar winner Jennifer Jones. After which, Caesar then took some roles on Broadway. Later that year, Bing Crosby's agent took notice and convinced Caesar to go to Hollywood and take a shot at becoming a movie star in what will be known as the "Golden Age of Hollywood."

After getting to Hollywood, Caesar started getting small movie roles, and with the help of his agent, he was signed to a contract with 20th Century Fox. In 1940, he auditioned for the role of leading man in the swashbuckling film, *Blood and Sand.* The studio had a tough choice, as the role was dwindled down to two men, one of course was Caesar Natale, and the other and eventual winner of the part, Tyrone Power.

Not soon after, Pearl Harbor was ruthlessly attacked, and the country was thrown into World War II. As all able young men of the day, Caesar wanted to fight for his country. As he was living in San Francisco, he immediately applied to the California Maritime Academy in Vallejo. Caesar would join the United States Merchant Marine. Eighteen months later, he graduated and took his first assignment as Third Assistant Engineer Officer aboard a Liberty ship. Caesar would bring the fire to the fight, but along the way would suffer the heartache that gave the U.S. Merchant Marine the reluctant honor of losing the most men, by percentage, then any other service during World War II. The enemy killed one out of every twenty-six men in the Merchant Marine.

Although very difficult to get Caesar to talk about his experiences serving in World War II when he was older, I finally cajoled him into relating one particular harrowing experience. After hearing his recounting of the chilling experience, I looked even further to my father as my hero and the most courageous and fearless person in the world.

It was 1943, and my father was a Third Assistant Engineer on a Liberty ship, which had departed from San Francisco bound for the Far East loaded with munitions. His ship was part of a fifty-ship convoy, and unfortunately for him, his ship was assigned the dubious position in the convoy in one of the end positions, known in the parlance of the mariners as "Coffin Corner." This is due to the fact that the ships on the ends of the convoy were normally the first attacked by the Japanese submarines. Normally, the convoys would be assigned U.S. Navy escort ships, usually small frigates, or "tin can" destroyers, as they were known. These escorts would patrol sweep forward of the convoy and then up and down the sides of the convoy. Realize that the convoy ships, Liberty ships, mustered the miniscule speed between five to seven knots with their submarine torpedo nets deployed, thus making very easy targets for the Imperial Japanese Navy.

One early morning about 00:30, my father had just finished his 20:00-24:00 watch and climbed up on deck to have a cigarette in the warm glow of the full moon. Suddenly, the ship was hit by two torpedoes and Caesar was thrown overboard into the Pacific Ocean. His ship went down fast as the torpedoes had a direct hit in the engine room with the boilers subsequently exploding. My father grabbed some floating debris and held on for his life. He furiously commenced kicking and paddling away from the area in which the ship was floundering so as not to be sucked down in the suction of the vessel as she was sinking. The crew comprised of fifty-five men, but only half made it into the water. The engineer who had just relieved my father not some thirty minutes prior had perished instantly.

Next, in the dark with the bunker oil burning on the surface, the survivors huddled together. They had hoped the radio officer, better known as *Sparks*, had enough time to send out the distress call before the sinking, so that the U.S. Navy escort ship would find them. Another thirty minutes passed, and the survivors began to see a silhouette of a vessel heading in their direction at low speed. At first my father was overjoyed as they were to be rescued, but that soon turned to dread, as it was the Imperial Japanese submarine that had just blown their ship from under them. One by one with a machine gun pointed at them, they were plucked out of the water. The Japanese sailors lined up my father and his fellow mariners on the after deck of the submarine. There they stood for what seemed like hours until dawn. Next, my father recalled, an Imperial Japanese Lieutenant approached the first mariner in the line. My father said he would never forget; the Japanese officer spoke perfect American-style English with no accent. The officer started questioning the mariners.

He asked the first mariner, what was the cargo? The mariner answered with his name, his position, and his *Z-card* number. The Z-card number refers to the mariner's serial number on his shipping documents. The handle of "Z-card" was coined due to the fact the mariner shipping documents started with the letter "Z." My father next said the Japanese officer was getting angry and asked again; this time the officer asked where the convoy was heading. Again, the mariner answered with his name, his position, and his Z-card number. At this point, my father said, he knew they were doomed, as the Imperial Japanese Navy were known not to take prisoners, but rather kill them instead. Sure enough, as soon as my father thought this to himself, the Japanese Lieutenant looked at an Imperial Japanese sailor holding a rifle with bayonet affixed and started yelling in Japanese. Almost instantly, the Japanese sailor charged at the mariner being questioned with his rifle with the bayonet and plunged his bayonet all the way into the mariner's stomach. Then, as if in one motion, with the mariner still attached to the bayonet, he flung the mariner into the sea. My father said, the man was still alive, although mortally wounded, and suffering terribly.

Without missing a step, and while listening to the death throes of the mariner in the water, the Japanese Lieutenant started questioning the next mariner in line. The same questions, and the mariner with guts of steel, knowing he faced the same torturous fate as the man before him, gave the same answers, name, position, and Z card number. With that, the Japanese sailor with the rifle and bayonet charged the mariner and impaled him as well in the stomach, and again in one motion flung him over the side, ripping his entrails out as he was hurled into the sea.

This continued on to the next man and then to the next. The brave men watched their fellow mariners face a horribly painful death. However, they all remained steadfast in their courage and commitment to their country. After the tenth man in line was brutally bayoneted and dying in the blood-filled water; the Japanese officer and sailors stopped and looked up. My father turned and he looked up and smiled, he saw the smoke on the horizon and knew it was the U.S. Navy tin can *pouring on the coal* or steaming full speed to rescue the men. Even more importantly, the tin can would sink that Japanese submarine. The Japanese sailors quickly ignored the remaining mariners on the aft deck and started preparing to dive the submarine. Dive, Dive, Dive, as the submarine descended all the while with the mariners on deck! My father and the remaining survivors started to jump overboard, knowing that they had to flee the area from the sub as she started to dive. My father said he heard one of his fellow shipmates yell to the Japanese sailors, "You're going to the bottom, that's the U.S. Navy coming to get you."

Once in the water, my father said they faced a new threat…sharks! That's right, there were ten men bleeding to death and filling the surrounding area with blood. Moreover, this was the warm waters of the South Pacific Ocean, prime hunting waters for sharks. Therefore, the survivors swam away from their hero shipmates. Next, my father said, the tin can was upon them, they were plucked out of the water, and taken to sickbay. In all there were about fifteen survivors. My father said he remembered hearing the depth charges deployed as he lay in sickbay. Later he was told, the tin can sailors sunk the Japanese submarine and the Navy sent her to "Davy Jones' Locker." Two days later, the U.S. Navy tin can with the survivors on board arrived in New Maia, New Caledonia and my father got right back on another Liberty ship. He told me, "You bet I was going back to sea!"

My father Caesar would also recount many amusing stories from his years at sea. One such anecdote took place in the South Pacific, again during World War II. As you can imagine, the men knew their days may be numbered, what with suffering the greatest casualty numbers during the war and all. As such, the little things at sea mattered most, not the least of which was the state of the food and meals aboard. With that, the men well understood the limitations of perishables, fresh fruits, and vegetables with many months at sea. This relegated them to frozen meats, poultry, fish, canned foods, and powdered milk.

On one particular Liberty ship, the mariners noted the meat served tasted odd or different. The Chief Steward, or simply *Steward* as invoked onboard, serves as department head for all the cooks, bedroom stewards, and hotel service utility men; he sought to make a name for himself with the office ashore. As he is responsible for ordering and preparing the meals, the Steward had wide latitude in food requests. Evidently, this peculiar Steward attempted to prove his merit by saving his monthly food allotment money on the backs of the crew. Ostensibly, the Steward substituted horsemeat for beef onboard. Both officers and men knew immediately something was amiss, again as cuisine is the one of two significant morale enhancers aboard, the other being overtime, which I will speak to later.

As one would expect, the men had enough, they set their plan in motion. It was a slow day aboard and the weather was clear and sunny. The great ship slowed and ultimately stopped dead in the water. The engineers, my father being one of such, claimed there was an issue with the main steam cycle propulsion condenser, which required immediate repair and thus had to be removed from service. In order to accomplish this "repair" the vessel must be stopped. At the same time, the Watch Officer on the bridge walked into the chartroom just aft of the navigating bridge, leaving only the *A/B* or Able Seaman on the helm and the A/B lookout to keep watch. The Captain was in his office toiling away at the reams of paperwork, which were part and parcel to his job, especially in the days prior to the invention of computers and automation. The scenario formulated a perfect condition in that all the officers aboard were fully engaged and gainfully employed in other duties. Recall, the engineers tending to the main condenser, the Captain up to his ears with files, the Watch Officer in the chart room correcting charts, and the Chief Mate in the cargo control center engaged with the cargo load plan.

With that, two burly A/Bs storm into the galley and grab the Steward, literally picking him up off the deck and carrying him horizontally on their shoulders. They maneuvered their way through the labyrinth of passageways, ladderwells, hatches, and doorways through the ship's house ending on the main deck. Unsettlingly and by some coincidence, the A/Bs somehow allowed the Steward's head to hit various structures along the way. Once on the weather deck, the A/B's, with the Steward now on their hip, meandered to the bow of the great ship.

Waiting on the bow stood the imposing Bosun, four more A/Bs, two Firemen from the engine department, and the ship's Carpenter, or *Chips* as was his handle. Prior to the arrival of the Steward, the Bosun and men had fashioned a three-hundred-foot mooring line into one continuous loop bending together the large six-foot eyes on each end. After such, the Bosun hurled the huge loop of a line over the bow of the ship. They then maneuvered the line aft by shimmying such under the bow and hull approximately thirty feet aft. To picture the makeshift device, essentially, a mooring line would lead down the starboard side of the bow, under the hull, up the port side of the bow and return to the deck connecting to the original bitter end of the line.

The two A/Bs hauling the Steward dropped him on the deck, the Bosun ripped off his shirt, exposing his bare back, and the Bosun tied the Steward to the long line, which ran under the ship. With that, the Bosun and the men *keel-hauled* the Steward. Chips then manipulated the Steward off the starboard side gunwale, and as he cleared the rail, the Bosun and men started heaving around on the line from the port side in a purposely slow and methodical fashion, as in "one…two…three…heave," then again, "one…two…three…heave." As the line moved in this herky-jerky motion, the Steward slid down the starboard side of the hull, passing by the ship's huge starboard stockless anchor sitting in the hawse, all the while with blood-curdling screams.

Finally, the Steward was at the waterline and the Bosun stopped, he looked down, and called out, "Steward…Steward…now, be quiet and look at me." The Steward ceased his wailing and howling, looked up, continued to sob, and waited. "We never want horsemeat again and for now on, we want only the best, even if you have to pay for it out of your pocket. Do you hear me?" The blubbering Steward shook his head in the affirmative. The Bosun gave his warning, "Now hold your breath." With that the Bosun instructed the men to commence heaving again. The steward immediately evoked his screaming. Then in an instant he slipped below the surface. The Bosun and men on deck continued their systematic heaving, one…two…three… heave, one…two…three…heave. In what must have seemed like an eternity to the Steward, but in reality, was no more than thirty seconds, he appeared, breaking the surface of the water on the port side of the ship.

Gasping for air between his howls, Chips looked down and shouted out the Bosun, "He's clear and bloodied up pretty good."

The Bosun smirked and remarked, "Now maybe we will have steak and lobster." As the men on deck continued to haul the Steward back onboard, his wounds were clear; when he was dragged under the ship, all the barnacles under the ship ripped up his bare back. Now the wounds were not life-threatening, but certainly emphasized the point of the "lesson." Once back on deck, the Bosun untied the Steward from his charge. Nothing was said by anyone, especially the Steward. Chips walked the Steward aft toward the ship's sickbay and nursed his wounds, dressed him, and warned him to say nothing.

Interestingly enough, as if nothing occurred, the engineers "fixed" the main condenser, and the ship was making steam again. The Watch Officer reappeared on the bridge from the chart room, the Captain concluded ministering to his paperwork, and the Chief Mate trekked out on deck. Nothing was ever mentioned, no one knew anything, and certainly the Steward never uttered a word.

After the next ship stores and provision resupply, the meals onboard changed dramatically. The officers and men consumed as close to gourmet dishes as was possible. In essence, the crew morale increased exponentially, and the Captain hailed the Steward, saying in tongue and cheek style, "Mr. Steward, I don't know what you've done, but the food has been unbelievable since the last resupply. You are making the crew very happy."

Another WWII Liberty ship sea-story which my father relayed dealt with a crewman losing his mind in a most outrageous and comical fashion. Once again, my father was on a Liberty ship steaming in the South Pacific Ocean. On this occasion his ship was not a part of a convoy and, in fact, they were heading back to San Francisco from the Far East to reload cargo. At the ship's speed of five knots, the crossing would take over a month. This day was a Sunday at sea, which usually meant, other than normal steaming watches, the men had time to relax a bit. Caesar was sitting in a lounge chair on one of the upper weather decks. With him were sitting another engineering officer and the Second Mate. My father looked up and noticed the Chief Mate walking toward them. Rather odd, though, was the fact the Chief Mate was decked out in his service dress blues uniform, complete with his high-pressure cover. In his right hand he carried a suitcase and in his left hand he held a briefcase. My dad and the two other officers sat back in their chaise lounge chairs smoking cigarettes.

As the Chief Mate walked past, my father quipped, "Hey Sam, where are you going?"

The Chief Mate in a lackadaisical manner, shot back, "I'm going home."

My father and the other officers started laughing, shouting out, "Oh yeah, right, you're going home... Hey, we want to go home too..."

The Chief Mate walked up to the rail and in one motion threw both his suitcase and briefcase over the side of the ship. Now my father and the others were really yucking it up, thinking what a comedian Sam must have been.

Then the Chief Mate started to climb over the railing himself. Putting one foot on the bottom rung and then throwing his leg over the top rail, he stopped and said, "It's been a true pleasure to sail with you fellas."

My father and the other men, now standing, fell quiet, as they had no idea how far Sam would take this joke. With that, the Chief Mate stepped off the railing, almost walking over the side. The men ran to the rail, but it was too late, the Chief Mate was already in the water. They couldn't believe it. He jumped off the ship. He thought he was going home. Quickly my father alerted the bridge who, in turn, commenced the "man overboard" procedures. However, it was for naught as they never found a trace of the Chief Mate. He must have been chopped to pieces in the ship's twenty-foot in diameter screw. My father would later tell me, the Chief Mate must have lost his marbles due to the War, combined with the loneliness of going to sea. I am certain today, that poor gent would have been diagnosed with that disease which ails many servicemen, PTSD.

CHAPTER TWO

"They that go down to the sea in ships, that do business in the great waters; these see the works of the Lord, and his wonders in the deep..."

- Psalm 107:23-24

I grew up a typical middle-class baby boomer kid; the last iteration of the baby boomers before generation X and the MTV revolution took hold. At around eight, I enrolled in a sailing program at one of the many Long Island South Shore sailboat racing yacht clubs on the Great South Bay. My club, Narrasketuck Yacht Club, located in Amityville, was named after the Indian river on which banks it resided. There were two such yacht clubs in Amityville, my club, bare bones basic, was all about racing, with none of the typical accoutrements of a Yacht Club in the strictest sense. There was no lavish clubhouse, no bar with a required monthly tab, no restaurant, no smoking room, no pool and no play areas—rather just a small musty shack of a building with no air conditioning and a few chairs. That was fine, because what my club did possess was all about sailboat racing and it's where I found my devotion...sailing, specifically sailboat racing. The other yacht club in Amityville was ostentatious, gorgeous, if not overbearing. Unqua Yacht Club was all about prestige, money, status, blue blazers, turtlenecks, boat shoes, Locust Valley Lockjaw, and oh by the way, did I mention money? Unqua had everything, except an abundance of "the hardware," as was the parlance of the sailors racing on the Great South Bay. The hardware being the trophies for winning sailing races; in Amityville, Narrasketuck most certainly had the hardware all lined up throughout its dingy little building.

When I mentioned sailing was my devotion, that may have been too lax a term, rather, I should have mentioned it as my life. When summer break kicked in, I would literally leave my house at 07:30, riding my bicycle some four miles to the yacht club and returning home around 19:00 — taking only a lunch my grandmother packed for me — oh, and a thermos jug with iced tea. Not the homemade stuff, nah, not for me — I had to have the tried and true *Nestea* brand sugary iced tea powder mixed in with water... Ahh, Refreshing! The "Nestea Plunge," as the ad touted. And yeah, there was no such thing as bottled water, other than by the gallon in preparation for hurricanes or power failures. Interestingly enough, everyone I knew drank the sugary iced tea powder mix, and low and behold, there was little child obesity. In fact, most of us were puny, or as my mother would say, "skin and bones." Maybe this was due to the fact we were outside some twelve hours a day.

So here I am, taking sailing lessons all morning and then mulling about the yacht club the rest of the day. I was trying to garner as much knowledge as possible from the other members, volunteering to crew on their boats, or what-have-you. A month later my father surprises me with my very own Sunfish sailboat. The Sunfish one-design class at the yacht clubs throughout the Great South Bay was a very large fleet, and very popular for racing. Here was a nine-year-old kid, barely weighing sixty-five pounds, trying to keep this boat from capsizing due to the almost constant prevailing southwesterly fresh breezes blowing across the Bay every day. I clearly did not have enough "rail meat" to keep the boat upright, rail meat being the moniker for weight. I also did not have the upper body strength to pull up and out of the water this one-hundred-and-fifty-pound boat after sailing. So, I did the next best thing. In order to practice, I enlisted the help of my mother. Between the two of us we could keep the boat upright in the stiffest of breezes. As for getting the boat in and out of the water, I had to rely on my boyish charm with the older (read: teenage) sailors.

Over the next eight summers, and winters with frostbiting racing series, I kept improving and winning race after race. By the time I was seventeen, I skippered the winning team for the Long Island Junior Championship and then went to the national semifinals.

Along the way, I worked at a local full-service boatyard, specializing in sailboats and sailboat racing hardware. This job was a terrific learning experience. I would work all day and then would race my Sunfish in the evening series and weekends. The owner, Stan, promised to train me if I were loyal and give him a good day's work. Therefore, throughout high school, I worked diligently at the boatyard, learning all about rigging, boat maintenance, fiberglass, paints, sailing hardware, and other techniques.

Part of my job consisted of getting lunch for everyone from the local delicatessen. For those unaware, there was both an art and a skill to the ordering process at a Long Island corner deli in the 1980's. Most of the delis on the South Shore were of the Italian variety, not like the North Shore of Long Island, which was home to the common Jewish or German delicatessens. First, I would get a list of sandwiches and cash from all the workers at the boatyard, about seven in total. Second, I would drive to the deli in the boss's van, I'm not taking my car for "official business," walk in, and wait on the line with the rest of the blue collar, union, summer teen workers, and "go-fers" like me. The South Shore delis were pretty much carbon copies of each other. Long and narrow stores with a glass deli cabinet and associated deli counter the entire length on one side, drink refrigerators on the other side with racks and racks of chips. Some of the delis had the occasional cured meat and cheese hanging down from a rack, a la old-world Italian style. The fresh Italian bread in all forms was behind the deli counter. On the top of the long deli cabinet there were sitting scores of various Italian hot and cold dishes and salads to go as well. The deli workers again were all the same type—big Italian-American guys with no necks, short hair or receding hairlines, clean-shaven, wearing dirty aprons and, of course, sporting the stereotypical Long Island wise guy dialect. And all of these "deli men" were equipped with a pencil affixed over their ear, like an architect or an old school accountant. These would be used later to fabricate…err…I mean, calculate the total bill. Finally, it's my turn to order; now you would think I could just hand over the list of sandwiches I had tabulated from the boatyard workers. Nope, I had to order methodically, one at a time. Moreover, any delays in ordering, looking at the confusing menu board hanging down over the deli cabinet, and dare I stutter or stammer, would not be tolerated. I would have been summarily dismissed, with the command, "NEXT!", if I so dared.

"Give me a genoa (salami), provolone, a little oil and vinegar, on a hero, with some mustard," I would bark out. Then the deli man went about making that sandwich. Maybe "sandwich" wasn't descriptive enough; maybe it should have been called a side of meat and cheese. The deli man would take out the entire genoa salami and slice about a half a pound or more depending how he felt about you coupled with his day. He followed this by a half a pound of provolone cheese. Next, he added a squirt of olive oil, some red wine vinegar, a knife full of mustard, then cut the hero on an angle, all the better to get it in your mouth that way. Finally, he would wrap it all up in that waxed white butcher paper, and by the way, no sanitary gloves were needed. Then he would say, "What else, pal?"—at which point I would go to the next sandwich item and so on. Now here is the real kicker: at the end he would take the pencil from over his ear and start adding each item up longhand on a brown paper bag. He would carry the numbers over, old school and all. No cash register was ever used, even though it was sitting right on the deli counter next to him. And every day without fail, even if the order were the exact same, the total tab would be a different amount. And you know what? I never argued about it. How was I to know what these "deli men" did in the evening after slicing meat all day? I just paid. Everyone just paid.

All the workers knew the deal too, when I returned to the boatyard, no one asked for their change back…ever, and no one ever asked how much was the total. They knew the drill.

I remember I worked very hard at that boatyard for minimum wage or $3.35/hour. After a year, I found out one of the other riggers, or yard boys, as we were sometimes called, like me was earning $5.50/hour, quite a difference back then. It was here at the age of fifteen I learned a lesson that would serve me well for the rest of my life. After debating with myself, I was determined to see the boss and ask why there was a difference in wage for the same job, and moreover, I worked for him longer and full-time in the summer.

I approached Stan one day after work, right before I was heading home. I asked, "Stan, Ryan mentioned he makes $5.50 an hour, and I only make $3.35 an hour. Is there a reason for the difference in pay, as we are doing the same job?"

Stan looked up at me, he was in his late thirties, had two children, an ex-wife, and a beautiful vivacious young blonde girlfriend. He was very matter of fact, sometimes even coarse, depending on his mood. One could even say he was tough, but if you worked hard, he was fair and consistent, which I also learned is one of the best attributes for a leader. Stan said to me, "Yes, there is a reason… you never asked me for a raise." I was floored, almost dumbfounded. Here I am expecting some lengthy explanation as to my experience and age or something along those lines, but none of that was the case.

Evidently, all I had to do was ask. So, I shot back at Stan, "All I had to do was ask?"

Stan, in his deadpan style, quipped, "What, did you expect me to just give you more money? What kind of businessman would I be? So now that you asked, you got it, just let Jeanie know in the office." And that was it… I just learned the greatest lesson for my work life. I realized, at that exact moment, I had to advocate for myself because no one else will. No one will sing my praises; and certainly no employer is just going to hand money over, especially if I do not ask. Stan had no idea that he provided me with the most useful lesson in work life in which one could ask. I never did talk to him about it, but if I ever saw him again, I would thank him.

Stan taught me another powerful lesson as well. One day I asked Stan if I could borrow the cargo van for the weekend, as I wanted to help my middle sister move from one apartment to the next. I wanted to be a good little brother and do this for her.

Stan looked at me for what seemed like an eternity and remarked, "OK, just leave your car here."

I acknowledged saying, "Thanks, Stan. I will be very careful with the van." Off I go and I move my sister. Everything went well with no problems and I finished up on Saturday. I would return the van on Sunday afternoon and pick up my car. However, on the way to drop the van off, I stopped at my friend Klaus' house to say hello. Unfortunately for me, I was not careful and did not judge the distance when pulling into his carport and in the process scrapped the passenger side door against the brick and mortar carport stanchion to the sound of metal grinding. I jumped out, ran over, and my heart sank. The driver side door and mirror were severely damaged. There is no way Stan would not notice such damage. I had to think quickly.

I blurted out to Klaus, "Don't you have a friend who is a body and fender man?"

Klaus, shot back, "Yeah, Tom. He has a shop. I'll call him up and see if he can meet us there. It's Sunday, after all." Luckily, Tom agreed to meet us at the body shop. Klaus and I jump in the van and drive the few miles to meet up with Tom. When we arrive, Tom is dutifully standing with clipboard in hand waiting not so patiently to write up an estimate for me. I hopped out of the van, shook Tom's hand and thanked him for meeting me here on a Sunday. At first Tom seemed somewhat annoyed but he quickly changed when he heard the van was Stan's. In Amityville, everyone knew Stan and his boatyard. Then Tom went to work and within five minutes he handed me an estimate,

$250.00. I thanked him and told him; I will be in touch once I alert Stan to my error in judgement with his van.

After dropping off Klaus, I made the long drive, well those four blocks felt like a long drive, to drop off the van with Stan. After arriving, I swallowed my pride and knocked on his door.

Stan appeared at the door, rather annoyed, "I thought you were just going to drop it off and pick up your car, we don't need to do a face-to-face turnover."

Sheepishly, I replied, "Stan, everything went well, and I was just about to bring the van back, but I stopped at Klaus' house and scrapped the passenger side door…But before you say anything, I went and immediately got an estimate and will pay all for all the damages."

With a heavy sigh whilst rolling his eyes, Stan said, "Let's take a look." He and I walked over to the van, he then surveyed the damage and quipped, "It was very responsible of you, and showed integrity in getting an estimate before returning it to me. Tomorrow take it to the shop and drop it off. I will call them to put it on my account." I thought to myself, wow, how cool is this, Stan is not going to make me pay for the damage. Just as the words "*not pay for the damage*" were entering my mind, Stan continued, "I will deduct the cost of the repair from your paycheck. It looks like you will be working for free all next week."

I shook my head in the affirmative and said one word, "OK." Then I eased into my car and drove off. Little did I know, Stan provided a valuable life lesson for me again. From that point on I knew I was responsible for my actions, regardless of intention, and as such must pay the consequences. Further, being honest and responsible is key in life.

My parent's amicable divorce when I was ten resulted in my mother and me living in an upstairs apartment in my grandparent's home—an apartment my grandfather had specifically built for us. My sisters, being much older than I, were long out of the house, living their own lives. It was a beautiful home directly on the Great South Bay, which afforded me the ability to have a wonderful childhood sailing at the yacht club and working at the boatyard.

For high school, my parents sent me to the exclusive Long Island all-boys Catholic college preparatory school, Chaminade High School. It included an extremely rigorous curriculum coupled with intensive interscholastic athletics, stern discipline, and strong faith; all good stuff for the young man learning his way in life. Oh, did I mention, it was all boys! Just what a pubescent young man needs…no girls. It certainly made for fierce competition both academically and athletically due to none of the competition for a girl's affection. In reality, the fact the school had no girls was not a hindrance to my dating availability. Evidently, I learned parents would move heaven and earth to have their daughter date a Chaminade Man.

Upon meeting my date's parents, several of them would say, "I am so glad (enter girl's name here) is going out with such a wonderful Chaminade young man, would you like to take her out in our new car?"

I would then reply with some overly sappy, "Oh Mrs. (enter last name of girl here) I can see where (enter girl's name here) got her brains and beauty from, thank you. I would be honored to take your daughter out with your new Cadillac." When we left, what they didn't know—the better.

Finally, the girl would go crazy if she got my athletic team sports jacket to wear. The jacket, being so huge on her, would look like a dress, but she didn't care, because it had that necessary wording… "Chaminade (fill in the sport)" in huge letters on the back and my name on the front. In fact, after attending ten proms in two years, I determined it was actually too easy to date girls being from Chaminade.

In the end it was extremely rewarding, and I had no idea at the time how attending the school would come back to me tenfold as an adult. Time came for college and I was set on following my father's example, so to speak. With all my sailing experience, boatyard experience, the choice was simple, State University of New York Maritime College at Fort Schuyler or simply, "Ft. Schuyler" as it is known throughout the maritime industry.

Fort Schuyler is located on a peninsula in the Bronx, where the East River converges with the Long Island Sound. It was originally built after the War of 1812 as an army fort to protect New York City from foreign invasion and naval attack via the Long Island Sound. Ft. Schuyler was later designated by New York State as the home for the Maritime College. Most notably, the school sits underneath the Throgs Neck Bridge connecting the City boroughs of the Bronx and Queens. I guess all the cadets were a bunch of trolls living under a bridge. For me, it was a perfect fit; I was recruited to be a member of the nationally ranked sailing team, I loved boats, and deep down, I wanted to make my dad proud. Recall my father was an engineer, but that was not for me. I would choose to go to the deck side, as my father would say, a Chief Engineer will never be the Captain of a ship. Besides, he would often cajole me, "You go be a mate, so you can smoke cigarettes and drink coffee on the bridge in your clean khakis, while the engineers do the work...," and always with a big grin. Interestingly enough, that exposed me to the good-natured competitive rivalry nature between the mates on deck and the engineers. This is a fact of life on the ships in the U.S. Merchant Marine and one which I will go into detail later.

Four years and 180 days at sea on the school ship plus another 100 or so days as a cadet observer or intern on commercial ships and the day came to graduate. It was beautiful in the Bronx that day and a pendant hung from the Bronx span of the Throgs Neck Bridge wishing the class "Good Luck." Afterwards we had a small get-together at the Lobster Box on City Island in the Bronx.

It was there I showed my dad my freshly inked license as Third Officer and said to him, "Hey, Dad, I'm like you now, a licensed officer in the U.S. Merchant Marine."

He shot back, "No, all you have there is proof you can pass a test, now you need to go out to sea and work and live off that license, then you will be like the Old Salts."

Truer words were never spoken. How that would come back to me over the years! Unfortunately, or fortunately, in the maritime industry nothing substitutes for experience. No class, no course of study, no manual, not even simulation will suffice.

The great master mariner, maritime educator, author, and authority, Felix Riesenberg said it perfectly, "The sea is selective, slow at recognition of effort and aptitude, but fast at sinking the unfit." That was a quote we cadets had to memorize from day one at Ft. Schuyler. It is as true today as when it was written over 100 years ago when some ships were still made of wood and propelled by sail. Simply put, nothing surpasses experience and patience at sea…nothing.

The Monday following graduation, I reported for my first day as Third Officer with the U.S. Navy's Military Sealift Command (MSC) at their Atlantic headquarters, located on the Military Ocean Terminal, Bayonne, New Jersey, in Building 42 on the fourth floor, or MOTBY for short. Why did I choose MSC? That's a question for the ages. Spring of my senior year at Ft. Schuyler along with MSC, I applied to several shipping companies and I even asked my father to help me get into his old shipping union. Shipping was bad at the time. Desert Storm was winding down and no more ships were needed for the breakout of military equipment. The best I could hope for was the backflow of military hardware from the war zone dubbed "Desert Sortie." In any case, no luck for me. The best jobs for which all the students were clamoring were with the tanker companies, especially EXXON or ARCO at the time. Those were the crown jewels of shipping jobs, two months on, two months off, for $50,000 a year as a Third Mate. Every single deck cadet in the graduating class applied, all 125, but only two jobs were offered, both to female cadets. Shipping companies were getting pressured to hire more women. So, all things considered, as all 125 deck cadet graduates are essentially mirror images, they chose to increase their diversity. No harm, no foul. I later was told both of my female classmates who were hired had quit within one year. Consequently, that left MSC as my only opportunity.

I had my MSC interview in the spring. My particular interviewer, I learned later, was a well-renowned Captain within MSC's ranks. He was their youngest to ever be promoted to Captain. Even more impressive was the fact he was selected to command the lead ship of their new class of ships...while still in his twenties! I could not get over how much he resembled the actor Lee Horsley of the 1980's crime drama *Matt Houston*; go ahead and Google it. He even had a somewhat southern twang like the character in the hit show. Interestingly enough, he may have sounded from the deep south but this Captain interviewing me was a Ft. Schuyler graduate himself and from the Hudson Valley in upstate New York. After the interview, he handed me a piece of paper with a job offer. I stared down at the paper for what must have seemed like an inordinate amount of time because the Captain had to get my attention again.

I looked up at him across the table, wearing my perfect service dress blue uniform, and he muttered, "You have thirty days to reply to the offer."

Without allowing him to finish the word "offer," I interrupted him, "I don't need thirty days, I will take it...where do I sign? Here?" pointing to a line on the offer. The Captain snapped straight up in his chair. I must have been the first one of all the interviewees to say such a thing.

He then paused, regained his steady southern-like drawl and Command composure, "Well...OK then, sign right here (pointing) and give this to Ms. Stanley over there and the Admiral will be sending you an official "welcome aboard" packet. And uh, welcome aboard, I guess." After handing my offer acceptance to Ms. Stanley, whomever she was, I slowly exited the interview room in an almost trance-like state. Maybe it was starting to hit me as to the gravity of what just transpired. I then passed a line of my fellow cadets waiting for their turn for an interview, everyone as well decked out in their pristine service dress blue uniform.

One of my buddies yelled out, "How'd it go?"

I shot back, my voice low and uncertain, "I took the job." Now I heard a chorus of, "What! You took the job—just like that? What are you—crazy? You don't even know anything about MSC..." They were right, I didn't know anything about MSC. Well I guess I knew one thing; it was a permanent job on my license as a Third Officer. I also heard from others that I would have to wear my uniform on MSC ships, oh and the fact they don't pay well, and you never get any time off—were also in the "rumor mill." But, what the hell, I have a job. In my head I heard my father's voice, "A bird in the hand is worth two in the bush," and "You need a job with benefits; you are off my insurance at graduation."

MSC is a U.S. Navy Command, which controls all the sea-going logistics for the U.S. Navy and U.S. Armed Forces and is derived of five programs. The particular program I was about to join, called the Combat Logistics Force, or *CLF*, is most associated with directly supporting the U.S. Navy at sea. This includes all the ships that conduct *UNREP,* or underway replenishment, which are the ships that resupply the U.S. Navy ships while at sea and moving. Examples include tanker ships, ammunition ships, stores ships, supply ships or a combination of these ships. Simply, the U.S. Navy warship would steam alongside the MSC ship about 150-250 feet off, the MSC ship would send high-tension wires that support hoses for fuel or trolleys for cargo and this would be passed from the MSC ship to the U.S. Navy ship. Moreover, the MSC ship would have helicopters that would also transfer cargo and munitions to the U.S. Navy ship whilst steaming alongside. Finally, the MSC ship will be an integral part of an aircraft carrier battle or strike group, designated an U.S. Naval Vessel, or *USNS*, painted haze gray, with a number on the bow and even have active-duty U.S. Navy and/or U.S. Marines stationed aboard. The only visible difference between the MSC ship and the U.S. Navy ship are the blue and gold stripes on the MSC ship smokestack and lack of any offensive weapons. As mentioned, MSC has program ships for other logistic missions, examples include military transport cargo ships, special mission ships, survey ships, towing and salvage ships, heavy lift ships, high-speed vessel multi-mission ships, hospital ships and so on. MSC's first iteration, the Military Sea Transportation Service, or *MSTS* operated from 1949 to 1970 when the command was renamed MSC.

In 1972, a study concluded it would be vastly more efficient and cheaper to have civilian mariners or U.S. Merchant Mariners man and operate the U.S. Navy auxiliary ships. For the next thirty years the

U.S. Navy either slowly turned over their auxiliary ships to MSC for full operation or they built mission specific ships for MSC operation to the point that by 2005 all Combat Logistic Ships were operated by MSC. That's it in a nutshell. Something I had very little knowledge of when I reported for my first day at MOTBY.

CHAPTER THREE

"Every man in this Allied command is quick to express his admiration for the loyalty, courage, and fortitude of the officers and men of the Merchant Marine. We count upon their efficiency and their utter devotion to duty as we do our own; they have never failed us yet, and in all the struggles yet to come we know they will never be deterred by any danger, hardship, or privation. When final victory is ours, there is no organization that will share its credit more deservedly than the Merchant Marine."

- Dwight D. Eisenhower, General of the Army

Supreme Allied Commander, Atlantic

World War II

hen I arrived on that Monday, I checked in on the fourth floor and was sent to the medical department where I was poked and prodded. But mostly, it was the old, can I "fog a mirror test." I later learned the medical staff was all contractors and they were reimbursed according to the number of employees seen. I remember sitting in the waiting room with three other of my classmates graduates of Ft. Schuyler who, incidentally, also took MSC jobs. I was called in to be seen by the contracted physician's assistant, or *PA*. She resembled a little troll or a Hobbit character, in her late thirties, frumpy, overweight and quite zaftig. Her lab coat was stained, she was unkempt, and her office was filthy. I sat down across from the PA in her office, which was attached to an exam room, and she started to go through my chart. She noted I had high cholesterol, something which at the time I had no idea. Then she commented that I need to watch what I eat. I thought, what the heck, here is this rather rotund nasty funky woman telling me, I needed to watch what I eat! Unbelievable, but that was not the worst of it. Next, she tells me to go into the exam room and remove all my clothes. I was a bit skeptical, but figured, ahh what the heck, she must know what she's doing, she is a professional after all… little did I know, next thing she is examining my genitals, and not like the urologist, either. She follows this by inserting her fingers in my rectum, but did not mention anything about a prostate check; moreover, what 22-year-old needs either a prostate check or even a genital exam for a job physical? Finally, after I am permitted to dress, she asks me about my sex life. I answered but that bell should have gone off in my head sounding, "Warning: Pervert Sicko Ahead!"

I then go back to the medical department waiting room and sit down, feeling a bit violated and confused. One of my classmates sits down after his interview and exam by the same Munchkin-like PA. I couldn't keep it in. I had to ask, "Mark, did you have the Hobbit woman?"

He responded, "Yeah, why?"

I then quipped back, "Did she roll your genitals in her hands?"

"No, God no, what are you talking about?" Mark said, as if I were insane.

I then followed my line of questioning with, "Mark, did she put her fingers up your butt? Did she ask you about sex?"

Mark looked right at me and, in a matter-of-fact manner, said, "Dude, you've been violated; none of that crap happened to me. What kind of place is this we are going to work at?"

I shook my head, sighed, and simply said, "Yeah, maybe." With that, I was then called in to see the medical officer for my final medical check out so I can pick up a ship. I walked in to find a small Asian-American medical doctor. He had a heavy accent and didn't ask any questions about my chart. He certainly didn't ask me to remove my clothes, examine my genitals, or put a finger up my butt. When I say this guy had the "fog a mirror" test, I mean he would have sent out the dead Bernie character from the 1980's comedy movie *Weekend at Bernie's* as fit for full sea duty. Later I was told he was called "Chop Suey Louie," but whatever he was called, all he did was ask me to loosen my tie and unbutton the collar button, then he slipped his stethoscope against my neck and said, "Heart sounds good." Wow, I guess he can hear my heart in my neck. Ok, well, that was odd, but what was next was ever odder. The MD then stated, "Stand up. Now jump up and down." Confused, I obliged, and then he said, "Knees are good. OK, you're fit for full sea duty."

I then walked over to the crewing department, a few offices away from medical. It was a large room, with no windows, filled with plain government-issued metal desks, but none of those padded cubicles, which became popular years later. Obviously, there were no computers, just phones, typewriters, and racks and racks of filing cabinets. There were different sections: DECK crewing, ENGINE crewing, STEWARD crewing, and SUPPLY crewing. Each section had several people sitting at their desks. Now, with the exception of one man, all the personnel employees in the crewing department were women. Not just any women, "Bayonnets," or "BBQs" (Bayonne Beauty Queens) as they were often referred, with the image indelibly etched into my mind. The vast majority were raised and lived in the New Jersey town in which MOTBY resided, Bayonne. They all had very big hair, perfectly 1980's-style coiffed, to the point where a woman may be a full six inches taller with her hair teased. Along these lines, they carried a huge aerosol spray can of Aquanet brand hair spray, complete with its ozone killing CFC's. They wore an abundance of war paint, err, excessive make up, especially eye shadow, and their fingernails were way too long. I always wondered how they could type with these huge appendages from their hands. Their voices were high pitched and, you guessed it, stereotypical New Jersey accents with the last consonants always cut off.

"How ya doin?" the Bayonnet would ask me as her voice tails off.

I would answer, "Doing well, thanks," to which her response was always, "I hea ya, I hea ya…" Then she would tap away at that typewriter with those arching nails doing all the typing, fingers and hands balanced in the air above. Their clothes were what you may call, "heavy-metal chic," short leather skirts, stockings, red fuzzy sweater tops, and at least four-inch pumps or thigh high boots. Now, mind you, the majority of the Bayonnets did not possess the attributes to wear such fashion, but that did not stop them. The BBQ's all started as "stay-in-schools," in other words, when they were in high school, instead of dropping out, they were given entry level government jobs with MSC at MOTBY. Then, interestingly enough, without college, they could continue to work their way through the personnel or HR department up to senior positions. I was always astonished how a Bayonnet, who may never have stepped foot on a boat, let alone a ship, with no degree, is going to be my supervisor. But that was MSC in Bayonne—qualifications not needed, big hair a plus.

The real story behind the Bayonnet brigade was the lecherous old head of human resources, Billy Bob Samuels. Today, with sexual harassment and sexual assault in the workplace finally being properly addressed, old Billy Bob would have been locked up or, at the very least, fired. However, back then, and mind you this is less than 30 years ago, Billy Bob preyed on women. Understandably it was rumored and not substantiated, but certainly known throughout the fleet. Billy Bob would bring in these women to work for him and, if they became one of "Billy Bob's girls," they were set for meteoric rise, sans any qualifications. Did that mean they slept with Billy Bob? Again, this is all rumor, but there were pictures of women sitting on Billy Bob's lap.

Clearly not qualified, I remember one such Bayonnet who was handling a worker's compensation claim for me at one time years later. When I never received a paycheck and bill collectors were knocking down my door, I found out that this particular Bayonnet actually stapled my worker's compensation claim to the back of another employee's form, thus rendering it lost. When I found this out, I went to her boss, old Billy Bob. Little did I know, this particular Bayonnet was one of "Billy Bob's girls" and a Billy Bob lap sitter—and maybe more. You can imagine that was not good for me, and old Billy Bob made me start the process all over again, my paycheck be damned.

So back in the crewing department, I go to DECK crewing and I see two people sitting at their desks. One is the only man in crewing, the other is an African-American woman. The man is taking care of DECK officer detailing to ships, whilst the woman is handling the DECK crew detailing to ships (non-officers). That woman, we found out years later, when she took over the DECK officer detailing, would take sums of money under the table for plush shipping jobs. She was never held accountable, and retired with a nice cushy pension and the thanks of a grateful government. The man calls me over to sit in the chair next to his desk. It reminded me of grade school, whereas the schoolteacher had the one chair on the side of her desk facing her, you know the one chair in which no one wanted to sit. So, I sit next to the man in the designated chair, a simple government-issued metal chair with green vinyl padding to match the government-issued metal desk, circa 1965. He introduces himself as Dominic DiBenedetto. He was in his late thirties, Italian-American, heavy set, with a receding hairline, impeccably dressed, looking like a character right out of the *Godfather* trilogy. He was also from the South Shore of Long Island and a graduate of Ft. Schuyler many years earlier, and had sailed with MSC himself until he met and married a Bayonnet from another department at MOTBY. I guess he decided to come ashore to live a normal life with his wife and start a family. He seemed a nice enough fellow. He spoke very fast and he had this very fast bouncing on the ball of his foot, knee moving up and down twitch as he sat at his desk.

He said to me, "I want you to do me a favor, I'm going to send you to the SHINNECOCK, it's a very old ship no one wants, but it's a Third Officer job, so you will get your feet wet right away, no training job for you. Do this for me and next time, I'll get you out on a brand-new ship."

I thought, OK, and said, "Sure, sounds great. When do I leave?" Dominic told me to go wait in the Mariner's Lounge and he will call me when all the paperwork is ready for me. But before that he told me to go get my daily subsistence pay from payroll. So, I perused the halls on the fourth floor until I saw a gaggle of, for lack of a better word, undesirables. I asked one of these malcontents if this was payroll. Sure enough, it was indeed, but it was very odd. It resembled a drive-up bank window, but we were inside a building. There was the bulletproof glass, a small slot under the glass, a speaker right above the slot and a microphone with a button to push to talk. How odd did this seem; I am an employee here, and I am treated like a criminal at a visitation window in prison. So, I pressed the button and asked, "Hi. Is this where I pick up my daily subsistence?"

The Bayonnet behind the glass was frumpy and nasty, and said, "Speak into the microphone." I replied again with the same question and she then, without looking up, slid some papers for me to sign through the slot. Next thing I know there was twenty-two dollars in cash.

Feeling puzzled, I pushed the button, this time speaking right into the microphone, for I wouldn't want to be scolded again by this "wonderful lady," and asked, "What's this for?"

Again, without looking up, the Bayonnet shot back, "Daily subsistence. If you have questions, see your detailer… NEXT." So, I guess that was it. I took my twenty-two dollars and went to find the Mariner's Lounge, still not knowing exactly what the heck this represented. Later, I was told, each mariner receives a daily subsistence when at MOTBY or in a training status to buy food. This is due to the fact that, when on the ship, your food is provided, and they obviously cannot feed us meals in Building 42—hence the money. It was a

Union thing as well, as all the mariners were represented by a particular shipping union. Sometimes when mariners would be training or traveling, they would not only receive subsistence, but they would also receive quarters payment for lodging.

This reminds of an incident years later when I was First Officer; the crew was staying at a hotel for a month whilst the ship was in the shipyard. One of the crew decided to take all of his subsistence money and lodging money for the entire month and buy a car. Realize, he doesn't say anything, and MSC foolishly believes these are responsible people. Next thing I know I am walking to the ship and I see the crewman sleeping in a car, I guess the car he just bought with his subsistence and quarters money. He then reports for morning muster and work, all disheveled, unshaven, and reeking of body odor. The crewman asks me if he can borrow money for food. I was floored, and when he told me he used all his money for a car, I just about fell out of my chair at my desk and said, "How did you expect to eat and live for a month?"

The crewman shook his head and in what I believe to be as truthful as this guy had even been in his life, and said, "I never thought about that…" You can imagine what happened next. He was fired from the ship, sent back to MOTBY and I never saw or heard from him again. I wonder if he had to pay back the money.

So, I enter the Mariner's Lounge—now picture the NYC Port Authority Bus Terminal smelling like a country outhouse. It should be noted, this was an all-hands lounge, not an officer lounge nor a crew lounge, as is required on the ships. I walk in to find one non-officer or unlicensed mariner sitting at a desk with a phone, his right hand missing four fingers. I was later informed that this particular mariner lost his fingers on a high-tensioned wire accident during an operation on a ship, so MSC gave him the job of answering the phone in the Mariner's Lounge. Next, I noted rows and rows of plush, but beat up, faux leather reclining chairs, which were rather disgusting. There were a dozen or so non-officer or unlicensed mariners asleep in these once nice but since trashed recliners, snoring away, some with drool pouring out of their mouths. Others were sitting at tables playing cards, and still others were complaining, which is a spectator sport for mariners. There was also a TV at one end of the Mariner's Lounge.

I walked over to another officer and sat down. All I knew was his name was Joe and he had been with MSC for several years and I had met him earlier in the day while in the medical department waiting room. He looked at me with sad, puppy dog eyes, and commented, "Dominic asked me to do him a favor."

I perked up, because Dominic had said the exact same thing to me, so I responded, "Is that bad?" Joe, responded without missing a beat, "Yeah, that's bad. It's terrible. He will ask you to do him a favor, and then when time comes to cash in on that favor, he will forget he ever made that promise."

I didn't say another word. With that, I hear a voice yell out, "*Natale.*" It was the man missing four fingers at the desk by the door.

I leave Joe, depressed, mumbling to himself about Dominic and favors and go over to the phone man and said, "I'm Frankie Natale."

Then the finger-challenged man, without looking up from his newspaper says, "Go see Dominic. He called for you."

I gladly departed the Mariner's Lounge and headed to see Dominic in the crewing office. Dominic handed me my orders documents and mentioned I will be departing tomorrow morning on a Pan Am flight for Panama City, Panama and I would be picking up the USNS SHINNECOCK there.

I quickly remembered to ask, "Will the ship's agent be meeting me at the airport?"

Dominic looked up, knee still bobbing up and down at a furious pace, and shot back, "No, you don't need a ship's agent. Just tell a taxi to take you to the Navy base." My face must have looked like a deer staring into the headlights of oncoming traffic, as I was confused. In school, whenever I picked up a commercial ship as a cadet, the ship's agent would walk me from the airport through customs and physically take me to the ship. This, no ship agent stuff, had me concerned. It must have been obvious to Dominic, as he impatiently said, "Are you OK with this. Should I send someone else?" Little did I know, he had no one else, no one wanted this ship.

"Yeah, I'm OK, I got it, thanks…" and with that I left Dominic's office, the Bayonnets, and Building 42 fourth floor behind and headed to my home on Long Island for one last night ashore.

CHAPTER FOUR

"I wish to commend to you the valor of the merchant seaman participating with us in the liberation of the Philippines. With us they have shared the heaviest enemy fire. On this island, I have ordered them off their ships and into fox holes when their ships became untenable targets of attack. At our side, they have suffered in bloodshed and in death. The caliber of efficiency and the courage they displayed in their part of the invasion of the Philippines marked their conduct throughout the entire campaign in the southwest Pacific area. They have contributed tremendously to our success. I hold no branch in higher esteem than the Merchant Marine."

- Douglas MacArthur, General of the Army

Supreme Allied Commander, Pacific

World War II

The next morning, I awoke, bright and early, got dressed, and made certain to wear a jacket and tie. My father stressed, as an officer, you always meet your ship dressed like an officer. I was a little skeptical, thinking, I never heard that in all my days at Ft. Schuyler but, he's my dad, I should listen, as he knows. After a few pictures, I load up the old station wagon with my one very large suitcase, which was a graduation gift, and my leather briefcase, which was another graduation gift. The briefcase, so important, as it housed my license, my orders, and my grandfather's prayer book from 1906, which he gave me, would never leave my side. I recall my father saying, "I am glad to see you're not going "tanker tux" to pick up this ship." Again, my dad had all the U.S. Merchant Marine colloquialisms down pat. *Tanker tux* or, in some parlances, *Schooner rig*, originally meant just "with the clothes on your back and nothing else," but that morphed to just the bare essentials and nothing more. Not usually a good thing for a six-month job.

At the airport I said my goodbyes to my parents and told them I would call when I get to a phone. The direct flight landed in Panama City, Panama at about midnight. Realize that Panama at this time continued to be in somewhat of turmoil as it had not been that long since the dictator and strongman Manuel Noriega was removed from power. After I landed, I grabbed my luggage and went through customs. They were stopping everyone and digging through their luggage. I showed the customs agent my MSC identification and my orders, and with that, they whisked me right through, never even opening a flap on my suitcase. I walked outside the airport to blistering heat and humidity, and I was surrounded by poor children begging for money. They were grabbing at my briefcase and luggage, and I quickly yelled out, "TAXI!"

With that, a man stepped up, shooed the children to the side, not before I gave a few dollars to them, although I had to be careful that they wouldn't grab my wallet. The taxi driver opened the trunk of a derelict 1970's era Chevrolet, with no identifying markings of it being a taxi. He took my suitcase, threw it in the back along with the spare tire, oily rags, and other trash, and then he tried grabbing my briefcase. That I held with two hands and he got the point—the briefcase rides upfront with me. The taxi driver then asked, "Where to?"

Now, I recalled what Dominic had said for me, that was to just tell the taxi, "Navy base." I was thinking, was this all it would take? Would the driver know what I am talking about? With that, I replied to him, as if asking a question, "Navy base?" The driver replied in the affirmative. Next, in what seemed like an hour riding in this relic of an automobile with the windows down, getting good old two-forty air conditioning, in other words two windows down doing forty miles an hour. I was sweating profusely. I guess I was not used to the tropics, and on top of that, I was wearing a jacket and a tie, as my father had insisted. All of a sudden the taxi stops at what looks to be a group of abandoned buildings. It's dark, no streetlights, and I could hear screaming and screeching in the distance.

Before I could utter a word, the driver said, "I have to run inside and get something, I'll be right back," and with that, again before I could speak, he was gone. Here I am in the middle of, I don't know, somewhere in Panama, alone in a steaming hot car, right after the overthrow of their dictator, an American, thinking, this is it for me. I envisioned a pack of assailants attacking me, *Scarface* movie style. All of a sudden, I see the driver, he jumps in the car and said, "Sorry, thanks, we go now," and we were off again. Another hour went by, and the taxi driver stops again, turns around and says, "Navy base over there." He pointed across the street to a dimly lit guard shack in what seemed to be the middle of nowhere. Next to the guard shack, was a vehicle entrance drop down gate, and next to that on the side was a big sign that read, "U.S. NAVAL STATION RODMAN, PANAMA CANAL ZONE." Even though the time was around 02:30 and I had been traveling for nineteen hours, through delays, mobs, uncertainty, and sheer terror, my eyes lit up as if it were Christmas morning seeing the tree with all the presents underneath. I rubbed my eyes again in disbelief, I made it, and I eerily felt at ease, as if I were OK now. I am in the U.S., for all intents and purposes.

I then departed the make-shift cab, took my suitcase and, of course, my briefcase which never left my clutches, paid my good taxi driver, walked across the desolate road, and strode up to the guard at the gate, handing him my orders and identification, "I am here to pick up the SHINNECOCK." I said with determination.

The military gate guard replied, "The SHINNECOCK won't be in port until late sometime today. I can send you to the BOQ, if you like." I had no idea what was the BOQ, but after an awkward silence, the guard informed me that *BOQ* meant "Bachelor Officers Quarters."

Ahh, that sounds nice, I thought. It would give me a chance to rest and clean up a bit before the ship, so I hurriedly answered, "Oh yes, that sounds great, thank you." With that, the guard called a white 12-passenger military van to collect me at the gate. After getting in the van, I was introduced to another Navy guard, actually a quite pleasant fellow from down South, who acted like a tour guide as he drove his way through the base, pointing items of interest out to me. Finally, after about thirty minutes, he pulls the van up to a beautiful small Spanish or Mediterranean style townhouse, complete with the red Spanish roofing tiles, stucco finish, and façade to match. There were palm trees in the yard, and no lights on in the house. It looked so nice and peaceful, and when I hopped out of the van, a warm breeze was blowing, almost zephyr-like in its qualities. The Navy guard driver said he would pick me up at about eleven hundred hours. I reached in my pocket and took out a five to give the young man. Well, how much younger than I could he have been, maybe twenty to my twenty-two? Nevertheless, I was from New York and I was Italian, after all, which meant the required cash tip for everything. I had to spread it around, grease his palm, you get it. However, to my surprise, the young Navy man politely refused. Huh? I shook my head and said to myself, "Who'd have figured…" Little did I know, outside of my New York bubble, no one really tipped other than for meals.

Next, I walked into the townhouse, went up a flight of stairs which opened up to a nice kitchen, a living room, well-appointed, and two bedrooms. I rolled my suitcase into the one bedroom and noticed two twin beds. I thought, hmmm, that seems odd, but whatever. I am tired, and I need to get off my feet. I did however notice a phone on a table in the living room. I thought I'd better call home to let them know I got here OK; I mean, who knows the next time I will be able to call? I sat down next to the phone and took out my trusty pre-paid AT&T calling card, complete with all the country codes and pin numbers to dial. Recall there were no cell phones, so short of a collect call through the international operator, one needed a pre-paid calling card. Then I thought, you know what, I am not going to waste this calling card, I'll call collect. My mother must have loved that bill. In any case, I called my mother and then I called my father—remember they lived at different homes. As always, no matter what time I called them, day or night, they were always happy to hear from me. After this I finally went to bed after setting the old clock radio alarm for 09:00. I would be able to get about four hours of sleep, or so I thought.

I awoke to noises coming from the living room and kitchen. Was this an intruder? Aren't navy bases supposed to be safe and secure? But I didn't move, I stayed in bed with one eye shut and one eye open staring at the door. Next thing I knew my bedroom door swung open and a fella about my age walks in and looked at me, clearly seeing I was looking at him with my one eye and said, "Oh, did I wake you? I am so sorry. I just got in, I was at the officer's club, my name is John, but they call me Jake." And with that he stretched out his hand.

Now, I'm not used to being awakened by strangers walking into my bedroom when staying in hotels. That said, who am I not to reciprocate to an outstretched hand, so I pushed back the covers, shot out my hand, introduced myself, and we shook hands. You see Jake, was actually, Navy Lt. John Dentry, who was transiting through on his way to a new ship assignment. Moreover, what I learned later was that a BOQ meant "Bachelor" in the strictest sense, as in, you're going to get a roommate whether you like it or not. This being the start of my affiliation with all things U.S. Navy, I had not the slightest idea such a living configuration was even possible when in what I thought to be a "hotel" or "lodging."

At eleven AM sharp, I was picked up by the Navy van and driven down to the pier to pick up the ship. Naval Station Rodman had one main pier for deep draft vessels, which spans about one thousand feet perpendicular to the beach. There was a gate at the foot of the pier to control access, and unbelievably, adjacent to the gate stood an authentic Tiki bar, a literal mariner's dream and a nightmare for the officer of the watch.

The van drove through the open gate halfway down the pier. I then hopped out, gave my thanks, and the van took off. The sun was at its zenith, with nary a cloud in the sky and a blinding glare off the adjacent waterfront shone in my eyes. It was blistering hot, like I had never experienced in my life, as the ambient temperature was in the low 100's, with not a whisper of a breeze, and the humidity must have been hovering around 95%. Simply put, it was miserably hot and humid. The pier was concrete with wood pilings running down each side. Tied up to those pilings were three fifty-foot *camels,* or floating stand-off fendering docks, on each side of the pier. Of course, I recalled, the Panama Canal Zone has one of the largest ranges of tides in the world. These camels would be needed to keep the ships off the pier with the tremendous rise and fall of the tide. There were bollards dispersed every hundred feet down the pier with cleats situated in-between. I stood statue straight in the middle of pier with my suitcase at my right side, my briefcase hanging in my left hand, wearing my chino slacks, blue blazer, tie, and Vuarnet brand cat-eye sunglasses, all the while drenched with perspiration running down my face…

I could see the ship making its approach to the pier as I stood there silently waiting, thoroughly soaked to my skin in sweat. The USNS SHINNECOCK was making her turn to come bow first with her starboard side adjacent to the pier, or in this case, the camels. I was very close to the edge of the pier and as the bow passed by me, I could see the First Officer standing up by the jack staff; he even waved to me as he passed. The ship knew they were expecting a new Third Officer, so I assume The Mate, seeing me in my Sunday-go-to-meetings and briefcase standing on the pier, must have figured I was he, the new Third Officer. Assumptions as to possible crewmembers from peering down at the pier can be embarrassing, if you are not certain of who they are. Even more reason to never "assume" anything, even at sea.

Years later, I remember one time when I was Second Officer on one particular ship, and we were docked in Haifa, Israel expecting a new Third Officer and a new Chief Steward. To put this in perspective, one has to realize that, generally speaking, most of the Chief Stewards, cooks, yeomen and supply types in MSC were of Filipino heritage. The gangway watch notifies me there is a new crew signing onboard. So, I make the trek down from the bridge, where I was tending to my charts, to go ahead and welcome this new crew member aboard and take him to his stateroom and the like. Now, mind you, the gangway watch never specified what position the new crew member would be filling; all I knew was the fact it could be a Third Officer or Chief Steward. When I reached the gangway, I noticed a middle-aged gentleman of Asian descent, Filipino to be exact. I shook his hand and he seemed like a nice enough man, and I asked him to follow me. We exchanged pleasantries in the elevator on the way up to officer country on the ship.

I then proceeded to walk him down a line of officer staterooms, to the one marked "Chief Steward." I then turned, looked at the new officer and said, "OK, Steward, here's your room." The seemingly pleasant fellow, turned into a fit of rage and shouted, "What, just because I am Filipino, you think I am the Chief Steward? What gives, a Filipino can't be a mate or engineer?"

I quickly responded, "Oh, I am so sorry, that was terrible of me to assume that – but… you've gotta admit, it was a pretty good assumption." All of a sudden the new Third Officer smiled, and I must have disarmed him, because he then agreed with me and actually started to joke about the entire incident. Interestingly enough, in the time we sailed together, he was a good sport, even laughing when I would cajole. On many occasions, when he would make a very minor mistake or the like, I would shout out, "Hey David, back to the steward's office!" It was all in good fun and everyone took it in the spirit of mariners at sea.

Now back to the USNS SHINNECOCK passing by me as she was docking. Next, I see the bridge which was located on the forward house, and I notice a schoolmate of mine from Ft. Schuyler on the bridge wing. It was Matt Thule and he was wearing his khakis with a set of what I called the "wraparound tinted windshield" over his glasses. These were essentially plastic sunshades, which one would wear over their prescription glasses. As you may imagine, they were quite large as to fit over a pair of glasses and even the arms were shaded, but in actuality, they were a poor man's pair of prescription sunglasses. Matt had graduated two years before me and had been with MSC ever since. He was a typical Irish-German American from Long Island, with a quick wit and a very dry sense of humor, especially with day-to-day observations. At school, he was my "big brother" and also my division officer on the training cruise, so I knew him well and I was happy to see he was here to help me if I so needed. In appearance, Matt was tall, over six feet, with reddish/brown straight hair and a light complexion. He was husky as well, and you could see he liked to eat – except for vegetables; he hated all vegetables. It must have been some regressive experience from being one of seven siblings and forced to finish lima beans or something. His one plight was his eyesight; the poor guy was almost blind if not for his coke-bottle thick glasses, which made the fact he wore the wraparound tinted windshield more palatable. In any case, I waved at Matt, and he noticed me right away on the pier, waving back.

The ship continued to pass by me as she was made fast to the pier with mooring lines. As I stood there, I looked at what appeared to be U.S. Navy active duty crewmembers scurrying about, especially on the bridge level. It was then I started to shake my head in disbelief. All the U.S. Navy personnel toiling about on the bridge or the flying bridge were…FEMALE! My eyes opened wide to take in what I thought was a mirage. I had no idea there would be girls onboard, and not just older middle-aged. These girls were around my age, and I counted ten just while standing on the pier. One in particular grabbed my attention, I would later learn her name was Amy, and I would find out she was the queen bee on the ship. You see, before the mid-1990's, female U.S. Navy personnel were not permitted to be assigned to combatant ships; rather, all they could serve aboard was auxiliary Navy ships. Recall, MSC's Combat Logistic Force was comprised of U.S. Navy auxiliary ships. These ships, although operated by U.S. Merchant

Mariners had U.S. Navy active duty personnel for communications, aircraft, and supply functions.

Next thing I knew, the SHINNECOCK was made fast to the pier with mooring lines and the crew was lowering the ship's accommodation ladder to serve as a gangway. When permitted, I made my way up the gangway with my suitcase and briefcase. I was met by one of the two Third Officers onboard, Michael Shorter, who was not the Third I would be relieving. The SHINNECOCK, as most ships of the day, employed two watch standing Third Officers. Michael took me to the First Officer's office.

The Mate looked at me, and before he could say a word, I handed him my license and stated, "Hi Mate, my name is Frankie Natale, here is my license, I am ready to work." That must have really impressed him because years later he would always talk about a new Third Officer who came dressed in a jacket and tie, handing him his license, letting him know he was ready to work. He would later credit Ft. Schuyler for graduating such a fine young officer. I would have to credit my father, as he told me how to dress and what to say when I picked up my first ship. So, the First Officer then took me to see the Captain. Just for clarification, the First Officer can go by many monikers, such as Chief Officer, Chief Mate, First Officer, of course, and/or The Mate, capital T for *The* and capital M for *Mate*. These titles are all interchangeable and used in different settings depending on those either formal or more informal.

CHAPTER FIVE

"It seems to me particularly appropriate that Victory Fleet Day this year should honor the men and management of the American Merchant Marine. The operators in this war have written one of its most brilliant chapters. They have delivered the goods when and where needed in every theater of operations and across every ocean in the biggest, most difficult and dangerous transportation job ever undertaken. As time goes on, there will be greater public understanding of our merchant fleet's record during the war."

- Franklin D. Roosevelt

President of the United States

September 19, 1944

The ship was the USNS SHINNECOCK T-AOK 1, which was built as an experimental class, loosely based on the design of the U.S. Navy's MISPILLION AO-105 class of underway replenishment ships built after World War II. At 40,000 tons the SHINNECOCK was 725 feet in length overall, with a beam of 96 feet, and a deep draft of 37 feet. Her 35,000-horsepower steam turbine powered twin screws with a single rudder for a design speed of 25 knots. The ship was painted U.S. Navy haze gray and had a big number "1" on each side of the bow next to the anchors.

The SHINNECOCK was designed and built with two "houses" or superstructures, one forward near the bow, which housed the navigation bridge, all the communication equipment, damage control, the Captain's quarters, all the deck officer staterooms, and the U.S. Navy military department's berthing quarters as well. The after house, was home to all the engine officers staterooms, all the crew staterooms, the U.S. Navy helicopter detachment officer staterooms and enlisted crew berthing, the galley, the different mess halls, storerooms, access to the helicopter hangar and flight deck, the smokestack and, of course, the engine room with the main engines and all the associated machinery.

The SHINNECOCK had two dozen cargo fuel tanks holding approximately five million gallons of petroleum product in a combination of jet fuel and marine diesel fuel. Unlike the MISPILLION class oilers, SHINNECOCK had a class I flight deck, with a hangar and all the support equipment for a detachment of two U.S. Navy CH-46 dual rotor cargo helicopters, or *helos,* as referred to in Navy speak. In addition, the SHINNECOCK had an entire hold or four full decks for 600 tons of refrigerated or frozen cargo served by one large cargo elevator. There were yet three more holds that could each be configured for 1000 tons of general cargo or ammunition cargo, this time with each served by two high speed weapons elevators. Both cargo and weapons elevators were used to expedite cargo to the SHINNECOCK's UNREP rigs to send to the U.S. Navy ships when alongside, getting resupplied or replenished. Throughout the ship, there were additional storerooms and the like for specific cargoes, spare parts, and canteen items also needed to support the Navy ships. Between the forward and aft houses was the "UNREP" deck and the "jungle" deck.

The UNREP or underway replenishment deck was a combined solid and perforated deck for water to drain down to the lower jungle deck, and included expansion joints. Fitted to the UNREP deck were all the underway replenishment rigs or stations to include both fuel and liquid rigs as well as cargo rigs, machinery, cargo and weapons elevators, cargo fuel hoses, manifolds, fork trucks and other material handling equipment. The UNREP deck ran from the bow to the flight deck, which permitted the expedited movement of cargo to various methods of transfer, either UNREP rig or flight deck for transfer via the onboard helicopters, called vertical replenishment or *VERTREP*.

The jungle deck below the UNREP deck was the actual *main deck* of the ship, or the uppermost solid watertight deck on the ship. This deck included all the tank tops or accesses to each of the huge cargo fuel tanks, manhole covers for tank cleaning equipment, spare cargo fuel hoses, and the watertight access to the cargo fuel pump room and cargo holds. The name *jungle deck* refers to the fact this deck had a series of beams, longitudinal and horizontal to support the low overhead, which was the UNREP deck. All the beams and supports made the deck look like a jungle with trees, hence the "jungle deck."

The SHINNECOCK had a total of eight cargo rigs as noted: five UNREP rigs on her port side, three cargo fuel and two solid cargo; and three UNREP rigs to her starboard side, two cargo fuel and one solid cargo. The SHINNECOCK's crew complement consisted of the master, five licensed deck officers, nine licensed engine officers, six staff officers, 70 unlicensed crew, two U.S. Navy officers, 26 U.S. Navy enlisted, six U.S. Navy pilots, and 22 U.S. Navy enlisted helicopter crew and maintainers for a total of 147 souls aboard. As for defensive armaments, SHINNECOCK was fitted with six mounted 50-caliber automatic cannons.

As mentioned, the SHINNECOCK was a class of one ship which was an experimental design to have one ship capable of delivering all the different cargoes needed by the Navy ships. Thus, instead of an oiler or tanker replenishment ship, a refrigerated replenishment ship, an ammunition replenishment ship, and/or a supply replenishment ship all having to supply one customer or Navy ship, one ship could be used for all such cargo. This would not only translate to less time the U.S. Navy warship would be involved in underway replenishment, which is inherently a dangerous operation; it would also allow the warship to return to the fight much faster. The SHINNECOCK was revolutionary at the time of its design, was built soon after WWII, and would be the precursor to the SACRAMENTO AOE-1 class of Fast Combat Support Ships. This class of four ships was delivered in the mid-1960's some fifteen years after the SHINNECOCK was built.

The First Officer, Neil Dashman, was in his late thirties, a 1976 graduate from Maine Maritime Academy in Casteen, Maine, though he originally hailed from Maryland. I believe he served as an officer in the U.S. Coast Guard immediately after attending Maine Maritime. He was medium height, medium build, with wavy brown hair with the most disarming voice and demeanor. After the nightmare stories I heard of brutal First Officers, I couldn't have been more lucky to have Chief Mate Dashman as my First Officer. He normally wore khaki-colored overalls, which would start out clean in the morning and winding up soiled by dinner, due to his intense work ethic. Did I mention he was kind and considerate, almost teacher or mentor-like in his disposition? Interestingly enough, instruction was his forte. Evidently, not too long after my arrival, Dashman would depart to instruct at the MSC fire school, and did a damn good job of it in the process. The First Officer did have a few quirks, I guess you could call them. He loved trains, all types, loved all things U.S. Coast Guard, probably due to his time in that service, and most significantly, he loved fire and emergency drills. He loved them so much, he even had a name for these drills…"Deck Sports." His tenacity for drilling, fire safety, damage control training, and emergency preparedness fostered a strong impression on me. In my career, I would follow his lead and become a drilling machine. Oh, the crew, as you can imagine, didn't enjoy "deck sports" too much, especially, in the heat off Panama in the Pacific. His drills would routinely go for two hours, when the normal drills last about 45 minutes. But other than those few eccentricities, Dashman had very little interaction with me, as I was so junior in the chain-of-command.

As I stood outside the Captain's office door with the Chief Mate while he knocked, I felt a sense of nervousness combined with a bit of excitement and adventure. Here I was getting ready to meet my first Captain on my first ship as Third Officer. On a commercial ship, conducting inter- or intrastate commerce, I would have to sign shipping articles in the presence of the Captain. These serve as a contract between the crew and the ship, and once signed, numerous restrictions and mariner protections go into effect. This is the origin of the term, "signing aboard" when reporting to a ship. With MSC, all crew members are full-time U.S. government employees, the ship itself is government-owned and government-operated and considered a public vessel of the United States. This is the case for all Navy ships as well as certain others, such as maritime academy training ships. As such, no shipping articles are required. In fact, my eventual best friend and mentor would always say, "We serve at the pleasure of the Command." In other words, MSC can send us to any ship on any ocean for as long as needed. A fact of life, which would come back to haunt me over my career at sea.

As I prepared to walk into the Captain's office, I contemplated that I always had an idealistic characterization of my first Captain. He, and at this point in time it would certainly be a "he" as in a male, would be a maritime academy graduate, maybe even a Ft. Schuyler alum, middle-aged with a weathered look, but very dignified and masculine. He would be well-spoken, witty, maybe even in an aloof sort of way; he would be wearing a neatly pressed uniform with eagles on his collar, clean shaven, with salt-and-pepper colored hair. He would be medium height and medium build and, finally, would be of the utmost intelligence.

With that the door opened, and there sitting in a filthy room, at a desk covered in papers that were in no real order and bedraggled, sat a huge Cro-Magnon-like man. He had the head of a bulldog, with the jowls and frown lines to match, the little hair he possessed was gray and in a comb over, and he had the body of *Jabba the Hutt* from those *Star Wars* films. He wore a way too small dingy, food-stained, yellowed undershirt with rips under his huge armpits. His immense fat rolls billowed out from under his t-shirt. But the worst was yet to see, for when he stood up, as I entered the office, he was not wearing pants; rather, he had on a pair of underwear, briefs at that, the old "tightie-whities." You would think this objectionable mess would have had the decency to, at the very least, wear boxers, being so inclined to go so informally. Nope, not this cretin; he was sticking with the bikini bottoms for men. They were God-awful, stained yellow, with blowouts around the legs and rear, including strategically placed holes. They were nasty and funky, again with his rolls of fat bulging over the over-stretched waistband between where the grimy undershirt ended and his beastly briefs commenced.

My first words to the man who I thought would be a romantic version of Humphrey Bogart, was, "Oh God, Captain, I am so sorry to bother you when your dressing…" I was being kind, because there was no way this "gentleman," and I use that word loosely, was in the act of dressing. Nevertheless, I thought decorum was the better part of manners.

Evidently, that phased him not, for he retorted, "Nonsense! Come in, come in. It's so freaking hot here in this hell hole…"

With that, the Chief Mate interrupted, "Captain, I want you to meet our new Third Officer, Frankie Natale from New York." I then went to shake hands with the Captain. I can remember his crummy hand was the size of a catcher's mitt. They were badly chapped, with fingernails almost non-existent, and moreover, no different than his uniform of underwear, his hands were stained as well. Next, I felt my hand being crushed inside his kung-fu-like crushing grip.

The Captain spoke, "Frankie Natale, is that like Frankie Valli? Are you one of those dago guinea bastards from the mob?"

My face must have had an awkward outward smile, when the Chief Mate quickly changed the subject. "Captain, it looks like we are going to start loading ASAP, I have the bosun getting the hoses ready to hook up and the booms topped and spotted."

"Very good, Mate, thanks...Now, what is it again—Valli? No Natale, I got it. Yeah, go check in with the purser, then get your turnover going. We're getting underway in a few hours." I looked behind me and saw that First Officer Dashman had already left the Captain's office, so I said my thanks, turned, and exited the office. As I shut the door behind me, I couldn't have been more disappointed. I wondered... where was Bogie?

As it turned out, there were great many more distasteful aspects to this Captain. It became overly apparent, Captain Don Stone was a classic *WASP*, or White Anglo-Saxon Protestant. In that he had no use for Catholics or anyone of Southern European descent. He was a racist and a bigot. Can one be both, I thought? Oh yeah, and he was a sexist and probably an anti-Semite, but I did not hear anything from him in that manner. I was told he only got to sixth or eighth grade, but it was clear he was a moron, and I mean that in the strictest sense of the word. Unfortunately, being stupid did not stop this man from advancing. How could that be the case?

As I learned later, during the 1970's and 1980's when shipping was lucrative and plentiful, MSC could not recruit many maritime academy graduates. This may have been due to the pay, or lack thereof, debilitating schedule, lack of vacation, sea time requirements before vacation, or a combination of all. Through these years, since the majority of the academy graduates went elsewhere, MSC had no choice but to promote from within. By the time I arrived, a good portion of the MSC Masters were what is referred to as *hawsepipers*. A "hawsepiper" is simply an officer who advanced through the ranks from the lowest position onboard. The term *hawsepipe* is in reference to the orifice in which the anchors are housed and, when deployed, the chain runs through as the anchor is let go. In other words, it's a tough place, so coming up through the ranks is thought to be tough; ask any Academy graduate and they may have a very different definition of "tough" to advance to officer.

In addition to the great deal of hawsepiper Captains, MSC had to go overseas and hire foreign naturalized citizens. Some of the more infamous MSC Captains hailed from Greece, South America, Italy, and Spain. They were brutal to their charges and ruthless to everyone else. However, MSC accepted that, for what choice was there? In fact, sometimes, MSC would promote their inferior officers without even possessing the requisite license. They used the public vessel statute. Captain Stone was this exact case. When he was promoted to First Officer, he did not even possess the requisite license. My hitch onboard the SHINNECOCK turned out to be Captain Stone's first shot at Captain. So, you can imagine my disappointment upon meeting and learning about Captain Stone.

Unfortunately, to the detriment of the few highly skilled and competent MSC Captains employed, many of the inferior MSC Captains floated to the top. What's that old saying, "crap rises to the top?" The ranks even included a few maritime academy grads as well.

There was one particular MSC Captain whose name was Daniel ("Don't call me Danny") Starmann. This fellow was truly in love with himself, to the extent he was often referred to as "himself." He even used to claim he "fired his first wife" instead of admitting she left him because he was such a jackass. Danny was in his late thirties, attempted to look like the Captain Morgan character from the Rum ads, with the goatee and blonde hair. He had a sadistic streak to him, and he actually was proud to demean senior officers in the presence of others. One time…he dressed down a First Officer to the extent that he fainted. Danny was proud of that "accomplishment." Leadership at its best. Well, on one occasion, Danny was given the temporary Master's job on one of MSC's most prestigious ships, a Fast Combat Supply ship, and he proceeded to run the ship into a pier at a naval weapons station. The pier eventually required a total rebuild at the cost of $300 million. You would think MSC would have demoted him for such incompetence. Nope, not MSC. They actually promoted him to permanent Master and gave him the lead ship of the next class, albeit in a roundabout way. In typical Danny fashion, he pounced like a hyena on carrion when the original hand-picked, highly-skilled and competent Master had a devastating medical incident, ending his career. Starmann came in like a hurricane and upset everything that the original competent and qualified Master had established.

Starmann wasn't alone in his ineptitude as Master. There was another such incident, this time with a Captain named James "Jim" Shaughnessy. Unlike Starmann, Shaughnessy was a hawsepiper from New England. He was in his early fifties and had the worst personal hygiene possible, in other words, a true class act. His uniform shirts were often too small and stained. He was crude in that he would scratch his backside then put his hand into a bowl of fruit, rummaging around before settling on a pear. One time, when he was Master of an MSC ship, he ordered the ship's communication officer to make copies of all the copyrighted movies aboard. You see the U.S. Armed Forces have agreements with the movie studios, and for the morale of the servicemen and women, the movie studios release videos of first-run movies, while they are still in the movie theaters, so those serving could enjoy the same first-run movies as the general public. It's a nice service the studios provide, free of charge. Obviously, there is strict control of such movies, for if any copies made their way off the ship to bootleggers, millions of dollars could be lost to the studio. Well, on this one particular ship, the Navy was pulling off all the studio first-run movies, and the ship would have to go out and purchase movies as anyone else and, obviously, there is no purchase of first-run movies. So good old Captain Jim Shaughnessy had the crew copy all of the ship's movies before they were returned to the Navy for eventual return to the movie studios. The fact the movies were copyrighted with FBI warnings all over the movies did not deter Shaughnessy. He forged on for, in his words, he was, "Doing it for the good of the crew." This is the mentality and judgment which MSC tolerates when it picks one of its Captains. The story gets worse, for the FBI is alerted, and Shaughnessy admits he made the copies, which is a felony. MSC, in the vernacular of my people, "goes to the mattresses," for Jim Shaughnessy—and actually promotes him! MSC has an admitted felon working as one of its Masters on ships that require top secret clearances!

Now where was I, oh yeah, back on the SHINNECOCK. Next, I made my way to my stateroom, I didn't have much time to sit and enjoy my accommodations; I quickly changed into my uniform, left all my bags and briefcase, and went to check in with the purser. The purser is a somewhat defunct position on ships these days. However, MSC still employed a purser, and even a junior purser, to assist in all the paperwork. The purser is akin to a combination of the human resources and accounting departments at a large company. The purser handled all the pay, all the personnel records and, in addition, all the paperwork associated with the ship—including ports, fees, customs, immigration, etc. Recall this was before computers, so everything had to be typed and records kept by hand in ledgers, hence the need for an assistant. The purser, like the cook onboard the ship, are the two crew members you want to handle with care and treat with kid gloves. One handles your pay and the other your food, so wise counsel is to tread lightly. That reminds me of a hard-learned lesson for me as a young officer.

A year or so removed from the SHINNECOCK, I was a young officer on another ship and experienced first-hand the wrath of a vindictive purser. In those days, in regard to pay aboard MSC ships, there were very limited options for a mariner to draw his wages, especially due to the fact there was no such convenience as direct deposit. The first of the options was the purser cutting a check for issue on payday. Amusingly enough, on the ship, perchance in the middle of the ocean days or weeks from any port, the purser would issue paychecks. The obvious question remained—how then will the mariner deposit his paycheck? Or in many cases, paychecks plural, as the ship is sailing for weeks or months without a port visit. I learned quite expeditiously to collect my paychecks and then mail them home at the next port visit. This creates yet its own set of additional issues—relying on the U.S. mail, and occasionally foreign mail service, for delivery. Once my check or checks arrived, I was dependent on a trusted family member to deposit such in my bank. Finally, hoping I had enough funds to cover my bills until my next paychecks arrived, I again entrusted a family member to write checks to pay such bills.

Drawing the entire pay period wages in cash remained the second option. All cash…that's correct. Here again, imagine being days, weeks, or possibly months from port, extracting your pay all in cash. However, this option added more wrinkles to the process as well. On top of the fact that the ship is some time away from any port and the ability to mail paychecks, now the mariner has, in some cases, oodles of cash without any secure method with which to keep his livelihood safe, short of a rudimentary padlocked stateroom wardrobe cabinet. Additionally, once paid, the purser would not offer to lock the mariner's cash in the ship's safe. Finally, it is apropos to mention the docks, or the commercial ports in which ships normally dock, are positioned in the worst and most crime-ridden sections. As such, when the crewmember drew his pay in all cash and departed the vessel, there remained a very real chance he may be mugged and beaten for his cash earnings. This scenario was very common in the years prior port security, as thugs were keenly aware of the fact mariners may be paid all in cash.

The third option on payday aboard ship was a monthly draft. This option was utilized by most of the mariners with families with regular financial commitments, such as a mortgage, car payments, etc. The company or business office ashore would send a physical check home for the same amount every pay period. Again, nothing was done electronically or through any direct deposit, as such did not exist at the time. It must be mentioned, this third option does not permit the mariner from drafting his entire pay, rather only a percentage of the mariner's pay was eligible, for example 50%. The rest of the mariner's paycheck would fall under option one or two, the remaining 50% via either paycheck or cash on payday while plying the seas.

The fourth and final option was referred to as the cash draw. In this option, the mariner may take a portion of his pay in cash and the remainder by virtue of the check. In this instance, only a certain amount was eligible for cash and even less if the mariner had a monthly draft as noted in option three. Quite normally, most mariners would have a combination of options one, three, and four. For instance, the average mariner would have a set amount drafted home each pay period as in option three, the mariner would then request a certain amount of cash, as in option four; normally in the area of $50 or $100 for use onboard at the ship's slop chest or ship's store or in port, as there are no ATMs at sea. Finally, the purser would issue the remaining pay via paycheck as in option one.

The one caveat to all four pay options: if the mariner did not specify his preference for collecting his pay, or the mariner did not pick up his paycheck on payday, the purser would, by default, issue the entire pay in cash to the mariner the next time he presents himself at the paymaster's window.

Returning to my situation with the spiteful purser on the other ship. We were in port and I was planning on being off the ship on payday. Notwithstanding, I preferred not to receive my pay in cash for a host of reasons, most notably I had no method with which to secure all that cash. As such, I attempted to be proactive. I walked to the purser's officer, stuck my head in the paymaster's window and explained the situation to the purser. I asked if he would kindly cut me a check and hold it until the day after payday when I return from leave. This purser was gruff and nasty, but after hemming and hawing, he acquiesced and agreed to my request. I felt pretty good about myself, being ardent and take-charge so there were no issues with my paycheck.

When I returned from the leave day, which was payday, I wandered back to the purser's office, again sticking my head in the paymaster's window, I happily declared, "Hello Mr. Purser. I am here to pick up my paycheck." Without uttering a sound, let alone a word, the brusque purser opened the ship's safe, fumbled for what looked like a small envelope and then shuffled to the paymaster's window. As I looked in amazement and utter horror, he opened the envelope and proceeded to count our thirteen $100 bills. I could barely contain myself, and blurted, "Hey, what's this? I asked you to hold my check. What am I going to do with $1300 in cash?"

The grumpy money handler shot back at me, "You know the rules. You don't show up on payday, you get cash. Too bad, so sad." Then he sported an evil smile.

I couldn't hold back, "I know. That's why I spoke to you on Friday, to hold my check. You said OK."

The old crusty ship's banker retorted, "I don't know what you're talking about. Here's your pay. Now leave." I gathered my cash and quick-stepped away. Seething with anger at the blatant lie of the purser, I walked forward and climbed the stairs, stood outside the Captain's office, and knocked. After hearing his invitation to enter, I did so, then explained the situation and what was agreed upon between the purser and me. With that the Captain picked up his phone, called the purser, and ordered the purser to issue a check. I thanked the Captain, who appeared a bit perturbed by the task, then excused myself. I immediately walked back to the purser's office, stepped up to the paymaster's window, and without articulating a word, passed the cash I had just received back to the purser. He never looked up at me, said not a word, and slipped my check through the paymaster's window. Foolishly, I thought to myself, "That was easy." Being so naïve, I further absurdly thought the issue was done. Little did I know the degree of spitefulness the purser possessed. But I would find out all too soon.

A few weeks passed and during a phone call with my mother, she mentioned she purchased a notebook computer for me. She went further to mention the IBM store was shipping it directly in a padded box. The machine was not cheap, I later found out, this notebook cost about $3000. Recall, this was before the internet and color monitors. The notebook was the precursor to the laptop, was monochromatic,and essentially performed word processing. Of course, the notebook included a 5 ¼ inch floppy disk drive to run what were the latest programs of the day. I was rather excited, as the ship did not have any personal computers, much less a notebook computer. Needless to say, several weeks later the computer arrived. At this point, I must remark that the purser's duties go beyond pay and the like; he is also in charge of mail. That includes picking up the mail, distributing the mail, packaging the mail, etc.

The notebook was delivered to my stateroom door. When I walked down after watch, I noticed the box sitting on the deck next to my door. I hurriedly picked it up, opened my stateroom door, and placed the box on my desk. Nothing appeared out of the ordinary, the box was sealed, but I could plainly see it was not handled very gingerly. Ahh, but of course—the post office and postal workers do not provide white glove service. I took solace in the fact the computer was professionally packed and shipped. When I opened the box, it revealed the notebook computer broken in pieces. Taking the computer out of the box, I opened the top to find the screen cracked. I was crestfallen. I could not fathom how such destruction could indeed occur from shipping, especially given the professional packing in a heavily padded box designed for notebook computers. The ship being at sea, I could not call my mother and relay the bad news. I certainly could not email her either, as that had not been available or even well-known. So, I did the next best thing, I took out my Kodak disposable camera and took several photographs. I figured I would need these for a claim, if possible.

Weeks later, after returning to port in Virginia and having the photos developed—remember there was no such thing as digital photos—I informed my mother, and she then filed a claim. The post office would not honor the claim due to the fact, they asserted, that once the package was delivered to the fleet post office for the Navy, they were released from all responsibility. Luckily, the store felt compassion in that I was serving my country and gladly replaced the notebook, free of charge. So yes, the story has a happy ending, although, I still wondered what caused such damage.

The Cargo Mate finally revealed the truth behind the mystery of the destroyed computer. He nonchalantly informed me the old miserable and malicious purser was the culprit. Evidently, when the computer arrived, as per his duties, the purser received the package and noted it was for me. The purser then proceeded to throw the box against the steel bulkheads, over and over. After this act of destruction, he sneaked down to the ship's weight room and dropped dumbbells on my computer package. Yet, this was not enough for this malcontent. Back in his office for two days, he would step on and shake the package. Finally, after days of torturing my notebook computer, and hearing the pieces rumble around in the box after violently shaking it, he delivered the package to my door. Curiously enough, I am certain, I was only informed of the miscreant purser's dubious deeds long after he had signed off the ship.

Returning to the SHINNECOCK's purser, he was an older man, say, in his late fifties; at least he looked that way: short in stature, medium build, from the Deep South, with the accent to match. His assistant was a middle-aged woman in her mid-to-late forties, best described as "rode hard and put away wet," an old phrase from horse racing, but it has since evolved to mean women who have been around the block and have the battle scars to match. Her name was Peg, and she too was from down south and nice enough to me. It turns out she signed onto the ship as a Messman, or a waiter, for the officers' dining saloon. Low and behold, with no experience or qualifications, within the matter of two months she was promoted to junior purser. Hmmmm, I don't know how that happened, just the fact the old purser was mighty chummy with Peg. I later learned that Peg and the Purser had been sleeping together...what a shock! Sarcasm intended. As time went forward, I learned a great deal about affairs on the ships, extramarital or otherwise, and how prevalent they were indeed. I used to say the ships were like the movie *Peyton Place*. Yes, even more times than not this was a method used to get ahead, not unlike the casting couch in the heyday of Hollywood. Boy, was I naïve! In the meantime, I had the unfortunate opportunity to experience the purser and Peg's dalliances firsthand.

As I started my *hitch* on the SHINNECOCK—a "hitch" being a mariner's obligated time aboard—I learned the elusiveness of a relief. In the MSC case at the time, it was six months before you could ask for a relief. In the commercial U.S. Merchant Marine, a hitch ranged from two months on most ships and sometimes up to as much as four months. However no others, save MSC mariners, experienced at least six months straight. Don't forget after six months of service, it may take another two months to actually get a relief, as MSC has up to two months to provide such. That equates to a hitch of at least eight months, more if no reliefs are available!

One would think after eight months at sea, the MSC mariner would get several, if not at least half, or four months, of vacation. For again, in the commercial maritime industry, a normal rotation for a ship's officer is one day off for every day worked at sea. In essence, after two months, the commercial merchant mariner would get two months of vacation after two months at sea, after four months at sea, four months of vacation, and so on. Oh, but not MSC, unfortunately; for MSC, the vacation was based on the government employee vacation tables. That's right—so the fellas going to sea for eight months or more get the same vacation as the government auditors at the IRS, who go home every night and have weekends and holidays off. That means it works on a schedule of time in government service. From zero to five years of service with MSC, a mariner would receive four hours off for every pay period, and there are approximately two pay periods in one month. Let's do the math. A new MSC Third Officer is on the ship eight months and gets four hours of vacation for every pay period There are two pay periods in a month…I can hear the old adding machine now in my head—click, click, click…and voila, that equals a grand total of eight days of vacation after eight months at sea! Can you imagine that? Even MSC couldn't offer that with a straight face, so they got Congress to offer a special leave called "shore leave." Now this equated to four full days of leave for every month at sea on top of the measly normal government employee leave. OK, here goes the adding machine in my head—click, click, click… and now the grand total of thirty-two business days of vacation for the eight months at sea. Since there are twenty business days in a month, it appears the new MSC Third Officer would have a whopping schedule of eight months on or at sea and one and half months of vacation! Wow, that's really bad, that's almost similar to the whaling ship days of the 18th century. I can readily admit after eight months at sea, I needed about a month to decompress before I can even enjoy any vacation. By that time, MSC is calling… "Back to sea for you. Why? You are a mariner, aren't you?"

Now back to Peg and the purser on SHINNECOCK. Part of my job as Third Officer was to assist the First Officer with damage control duties. One day I was assigned to go into each stateroom or berthing and check the *EEBD* expiration dates. "EEBD" is one of those million

Navy acronyms and stood for Emergency Escape Breathing Device. It was, essentially, a hood with an oxygen generator system, good for about 15 minutes of oxygen in order to get outside and in fresh air. They were stowed in a small box next to each bunk. To access the EEBD, one would have to open the storage box and pull out the EEBD. My method to checking was simple. I would first go in every stateroom on a particular level of the ship, pull out the EEBD, then sit down and check all expiration dates, finally returning the EEBDs to each stateroom. This would limit my time in personal staterooms, as I wanted to respect each crewmember's privacy. Obviously, I would knock to see if the stateroom were empty before going inside and, it should be noted, no one locked their doors at sea, unless they were inside.

With that bit of background, I knocked on the purser's stateroom door. I received no answer, so I proceeded into the room. I didn't bother turning on the overhead lights, rather, I just reached my hand into the EEBD storage box to open the handle and, with that, I felt, for lack of better words, a cold, gooey, gel-like substance. I knew right away. I looked, and in my hand was a used condom, filled with a substance. Yuck! I can't believe it, it's all over my hand—the condom exploded right in my hand! unbelievable! So, I run out of the purser's stateroom, go right into the officer's self-service laundry room, head right for the deep sink, and shove my hand under the water running at full blast. The condom washes from my hand into the bottom of the deep sink, my hand is clear of contents, but I still feel the slime. Maybe it was in my head, I don't know. I looked up on a secure shelf above the deep sink, and there it was—bleach. Yes, good old Clorox bleach. I took it and poured it over my hand, rubbing profusely. I would have used acid if available.

As I am working feverishly over the deep sink, decontaminating my hands, in walks Second Officer Matt, who blurted out, "You gotta be more careful. You know Peg and the purser are doing the nasty. Where do you expect they put the remains from bumping ugly's? They can't flush raincoats, you know; that would stop up the whole sanitation system."

I looked up as my hands were alternating between cooling from the pour of the bleach to burning once the bleach started to sting, and shot back, "What the heck is going on here? what kind of place is this? Couldn't they at least wrap it up in a tissue and put it in the garbage?"

Outside of their intended use, condoms onboard ship have provided their share of comic relief. Years later, I was onboard another vessel. This time the vessel was a new build, or new construction. Think back to the SHINNECOCK, as she was a very old ship, built just after WWII. There was a profusion of differences between old and new ships, yet the workings of the "heads," or toilets, by far provided an interesting dichotomy. The older ships were fitted with wet seawater firemain systems. So, in addition to having fully pressurized fire-fighting seawater at each fire station onboard, other hydraulic ship systems operated off the fully pressurized firemain. I mean "hydraulic" in the rigid sense, as in water-powered.

For explanation purposes, a "firemain" is the set of piping, valves, fire stations, and pumps spanning throughout the ship. Simply put, there is a large sea suction intake on the bottom of the ship's hull, from this sea suction there is a pump or pumps, then connected to the pump(s) is the vast system of piping in which the seawater is pumped to the fire stations. Think of a human circulatory system with the heart and its connecting arteries, veins, and capillaries. Further, depending on the ship, there may be over one hundred fire stations. Do not think of a fire station as in the town firehouse. Onboard the fire stations consist of a hydrant valve, a set of hoses connected to the valve, nozzles, and some bulkhead-mounted or wall-mounted tools. Finally, as mentioned, a wet firemain system also employs other ship systems which run on pressurized seawater. One such system is the head flushing system. The seawater through the wet firemain is used to flush all the toilets aboard. I should mention, the use of such pressurized seawater requires all the heads to have commercial flushometers to regulate such pressure. This system provides quite a great deal of flushing power. In addition, the sewage piping system is vast and large, some with diameters of two inches. As such, there is rarely a clogged toilet or sewage system piping section. You could literally insert a handful of golf balls and there would be no issues with flushing.

In stark contrast resides the head system on the new ships. Unlike the older ships which operate off their wet firemain, the new ships do not have a wet firemain, and thus their heads operate off a vacuum and freshwater system. Essentially, the ship has a colossal vacuum attached to the sewage piping system with pipes only ¼ inch in diameter. When mariners use the head, they press a vacuum activation button on the back of the commode, which in turn, opens the valve and vacuum draws the effluent in the bowl into the piping system about six inches. Immediately, added to the bowl is a cup full of fresh water used primarily as an odor water-seal. This is designed to prevent sewage odors from emanating. Just a little hint, it does a very poor job. Only a cup of water is permitted because fresh water is a finite commodity aboard ship. The real sticking point in this system, no pun intended, is the size of the pipes and the mechanism which only moves the effluent about six inches per flush. With such restrictions, imperative actions must be appropriated to ensure nothing goes into the bowl which didn't go first through the human body. Now bring forth the condom or the feminine hygiene product, but especially the condom. If a reluctant crewmember decides to flush a condom down the vacuum head to hide his or her dalliances, he or she risks plugging up the entire system. Unfortunately, this is more common than one may think.

Tasked with fixing the clogged heads is the Third Assistant Engineering officer, fondly dubbed the "Turd Chaser," for obvious reasons. This poor soul must locate the leg of the piping system in which the condom is blocking the vacuum system. Once the area is marked, the Third Engineer must then cut and remove the blocked area and snake the piping system. Don't forget after removing the condom, he must clear out the backed up raw sewage effluent sitting in the pipe. Feeling ill yet? Next, after thoroughly snaking and cleaning the piping, the Third Engineer must replace the section. The next undeniable question remains, what happened to the condom which caused the blockage? One may assume, the Third Engineer would dispose of such in a proper receptacle. One may think that, and one would be wrong. No, the Third Engineer, frustrated, angry, disgusted, and worse, prominently affixes the condom in all its sewage glory, in the personnel elevator so the entire crew may witness the fruits of his labor. YUCK! By the way, the Third Engineer will use the same modus operandi for any feminine hygiene products blocking the vacuum sewage system.

Back on the SHINNECOCK...after checking in with the purser and Peg, the assistant purser, I met up with the Third Officer who I would be relieving. After eight months, I am sure he was more than ready to go. As it turned out, ostensibly he was not being relieved as much as he was being fired, and I was his replacement. His name was Taylor Redsen, he was African-American which, with bulldog CAPT Stone, must have been difficult. Redsen was also a bit older than I, maybe in his late twenties. Taylor was a hawsepiper, a former Navy enlisted man, and this was his first job as Third Officer. I remember he seemed nice enough, was of medium height, well-built, personable, very gregarious, and the word player or "playa" came to mind, as in a dubious lady's man. He also had one of those late eighties, early nineties popular African-American hairstyles, similar to actor Will Smith's *Fresh Prince of Bellaire*, or as some referred to it, as the "eraser head" haircut, as the sides were tight and top very high, rather unusually high.

Being from the South Shore of Long Island, I did not have much interaction with black folks, so this was pretty much new to me. He and I sat down at the fantail mooring area on a couple of *bitts*. The fantail mooring area is the extreme back of the ship where the mooring lines and winches are located; bitts are the two-horned structures in which mooring lines are made fast. They are the size of stools, so often mariners sit on them and look out at the sea. So here, Taylor and I were, but he wasn't giving me what I would call a thorough turnover. In fact, he gave me no turnover at all except to say, with a grin from ear to ear, "You're gonna love this ship!" I didn't know how to respond, so I didn't, and the next thing I know, Taylor is getting up and leaving, saying, "Well, I gotta go. See ya 'round," and he was gone.

I thought, just as well, I need to get acclimated, so I went to the bridge. I knew we were getting underway soon and I wanted to familiarize myself with all the bridge equipment as well as read and sign the

Master's standing orders. While up on the bridge I ran into Matt, the Second Officer, and finally got a chance to talk to him. He explained that they were expecting me and that he put the good word in for me. Uh oh, that's never a good thing. I didn't want the good word. In fact, I didn't want any word. I'd rather be wordless coming aboard. Then Matt told me about the ship, how it was a good ship, and our run for the next foreseeable future is supporting *LEO* or the U.S. Navy's Law Enforcement Operations, which was the Navy's part of the 1980's war on drugs. We would support all the Navy ships interdicting the drug-running boats from South and Central America into the U.S. Our resupply would be in and out right here at Naval Station Rodman in Panama. All in all, I thought, that's not too bad. The naval station is like being back in the States. There was a U.S. Post Office, an exchange similar to a Target store, a convenience store similar to a 7-11, a car rental for those who would venture out, barbershop, different clubs (depending on rank), a yacht club with boat rentals, one lonely Pizza Hut and, most importantly, a phone center to call home. I thought I could handle this every week, sort of a basic resort without all the creature comforts.

Now the bridge of the SHINNECOCK was not what I was expecting, albeit with my years and years of sea-going experience at the time – sarcasm alarm going off. It was long and narrow going *athwartships* or, across ship. I'd say it ran about sixty to seventy feet across and ten to fifteen feet deep from the portholes to the door to the chart room on the after *bulkhead* or wall. Remember, this ship was built not long after WWII, so right off the bat, there was no air conditioning on the bridge. AC was later added to parts of the ship, but never the bridge. Yup, instead, the bridge had ten literal portholes, which could be opened for fresh air, sealed shut, and/or even blacked out with a steel blank. Two things right away about portholes on a bridge: for optimal visibility, that being first off, there is very little visibility out of small eighteen-inch portholes, and second, they only provide air when open. On each side of the bridge, there stood an old-fashioned six-dog class 1 watertight door, which was of the blast-resistant type, in other words, heavy with a capital H. There was no visibility aft on the bridge because the chart room and the radio room were behind the bridge.

There were no large windows as well, not even on the sides near the watertight doors to the bridge wings.

The equipment on the bridge was bare bones as well; on the starboard side, we had one Raytheon RAYCAS X-band cathode ray tube commercial radar with very limited collision avoidance functions. In addition, on the port side we had a military SPS-10, G-band radar that actually still utilized vacuum tubes, which was pretty much useless for determining risk of collision as per the Rules of the Road. At least the RAYCAS was solid state. Curiously, one would think radars and expensive electronic navigation equipment should be kept in a climate-controlled area, i.e. air conditioning. I guess the bridge not having AC must have contributed to the water pouring out from the radar cabinet on one occasion. Imagine, a radar running off 440 volts with water pouring out on the deck, and I am standing on the deck. I'm lucky I wasn't fried right there with my face inside the radar's hood. As it turned out, the water was from all the condensation caused by the heat generated by the radar combined with the ambient high temperatures and almost 100% humidity on the bridge sans AC.

Directly centerline on the bridge, the SHINNECOCK had a true telemotor ship's wheel. This was a beast, at five feet in diameter with the top damn near as high as I am tall. Steering with this, one would feel like he was on an old clipper ship sailing across the Atlantic. Now a telemotor helm uses hydraulic fluid and pumping action within the helm to send the fluid all the way down to the six-way valve in the steering engine room, which sat atop the rudderstock and operated the huge hydraulic rams, which in turn would move the rudder. So, every time the helmsman would turn the telemotor ship's wheel, he would actually be pumping hydraulic fluid all the way down to the rams which move the rudder. As you can imagine there are limitations such as the viscosity of the hydraulic fluid, the speed or rate of the turn of the helm corresponding with that of the actual rudder stock. Adjacent to starboard of the telemotor helm was the hand electric helm console. This consisted of a stand with a small ship's wheel the size of a car steering wheel, as well as some controls for automatic steering. This was called the "iron mike" or just "the mike." This wheel was much,

much smaller because it was not a pump moving hydraulic fluid to the six-valve to move the rams. Rather, the hand electric would send an electric signal down to the six-way valve, which would then direct the hydraulic rams to move the rudder. The hand electric with automatic controls was considered state-of-the-art.

Nevertheless, old Jabba the Hut was too, I don't know, what's the word… foolish, idiotic, moronic, what have you, to ever use the damn thing. No, not this genius, he had these poor helmsmen toil away on the telemotor, physically moving the hydraulic fluid manually via the ship's wheel. It's not an exaggeration to have a helmsman drenched in sweat after an hour and half on the wheel in any type of sea. I guess I neglected to mention, at this time in history, Captains were judge, jury, and executioner onboard—the last true autocracy remaining. This, of course, would change within the next fifteen years with the advent of the internet, email, and satellite phones. But when I signed aboard SHINNECOCK, the Captain's word was Gospel and once the ship was out of sight of land, there was no recourse.

On the far starboard side of the bridge was a chart table equipped with two chronometers, a LORAN-C near coastal positioning device, good to about 500 miles off the U.S. coast, not good where we were located, far from the U.S. mainland. We also had a first-generation transit satellite navigation system or NAVSAT. This was satellite navigation in its infancy, and NAVSAT would require the tracking of the satellite as it passed overhead. However, elevation requirements coupled with the Doppler effect plagued the system, sometimes not providing accurate positions for several days and then at times even providing inaccurate positions. In addition, the SHINNECOCK had older electronics such as DECCA and OMEGA, all coastal navigation positioning systems. The deck was covered with old asbestos tiles and the *overhead* or ceiling was not covered with a beautiful drop-down façade, no, rather all the pipes, wires, and cableways were right overhead exposed. The after-bulkhead had rows of bells and amplifiers, controls, fire alarms, voice tubes if you can believe it, and ships damage control isometric drawings.

For compasses, we had a tried and true magnetic compass located on the flying bridge, which is the deck over the navigating bridge, which the helmsman could view through a periscope whilst standing at the telemotor helm. We also had two Anschutz Kiel Gyrocompasses, which were located in the chartroom, with repeaters on both helm stands, on the bridge wings, also directly under the forward most centerline porthole, and in other areas about the ship. An interesting historical fact was the gyro repeaters had the wording *Built by the Chrysler Corporation for the U.S. Navy* embossed into the outermost ring. Although it was strange to see one of Detroit's big three automakers named on a piece of navigational equipment, it made sense as this ship was launched soon after WWII and the builders must have used surplus equipment; and in wartime, all the car manufacturers shifted to the war effort. I thought it really tied the ship back to the Second World War.

As I was going through the bridge equipment, up walks Michael, the other Third Officer, who had met me at the gangway when I boarded the SHINNECOCK. Michael was medium height but with a stocky build; he was about ten years older than I, and this was his first ship as Third Officer as well. He was a genuine person, an evangelical Christian, although he didn't wear it on his sleeve. He was kind, genuine, considerate as mentioned, and pleasant to everyone; of course, they made his life a living hell.

I had a tremendous amount of respect for Michael. You see, he graduated from Kings Point, the federal maritime academy, and then he worked directly for a giant defense contractor in the testing and trials division. He explained he was in charge of testing the canopies of fighter jet aircraft for the ability to withstand possible bird strikes. I figured there must have been some high-tech metric, gas spectrometer, gobbledygook-type machine to perform such a test. Not the case. Michael told me he would simply shoot frozen chickens through a large bored gun directly at the canopy. Captain Bulldog and some of the malcontent officers would call Michael the "Chicken Man" due to this. He took it as good honest ribbing, but Jabba and his sycophants were just plain mean and nasty.

Michael had this job for over ten years with this large defense contractor out in the Midwest. He had a wife and two young boys. He wasn't making oodles of money, but he was doing fine supporting his small family. Unfortunately, after about ten years of work, the defense contractor laid off Michael. Now having no job and a family to feed, he figured he would go ahead and use that license he was awarded so many years ago at Kings Point. He, of course, got a job with MSC. I am certain it must have been immensely difficult for him after a dozen years of not being in the industry and, on top of that, leaving your family for at least eight months after they had him home every night. I credit him for adhering to the mantra, "a man's got to do what a man's got to do," for his family. "La famiglia," we say in Italian, "The Family." That being said, poor Michael had it tough. MSC deck officers bite when they see blood in the water, and Michael's weaknesses of not being in the industry were like chum in the water for the bloodthirsty, backstabbing, deck officers at MSC. Poor Michael found that out.

I stayed on the bridge until dinner. I heard we were getting underway at 20:00 or eight PM, for those military time-challenged. Matt took me down to dinner and told me where to sit in the officers' saloon. In the U.S. Merchant Marine, the *saloon* is where the officers dine, a very dignified and refined name, which brings visions of three-course meals, fine china, tablecloths, and linen napkins. The U.S. Navy calls it the officers' mess, or wardroom. I preferred to dine in a saloon; I hoped the food was as good as the name of the dining facility. We walked into the saloon and there were six tables with four seats each and one round table with eight seats, which was the Master's table.

Some people ashore, and even some U.S. Navy officers, get the terms "Master" and "Captain" confused. However, it's quite easy to differentiate. The term *Master* is the title, while the term *Captain* is the rank. Knowing those subtleties, it should be quite clear. For instance, on a U.S. Navy aircraft carrier, the person in overall command is titled "Commanding Officer," but his rank is "Captain." People on the ship do not address him as "Commanding Officer," rather they would say "Captain." The same holds true in the U.S. Merchant Marine. No one is going around addressing the Captain as "Master," but it's his title.

That reminds me of an incident which occurred some years later when I was the Master of my own underway replenishment ship transiting the Suez Canal as part of an aircraft carrier battlegroup. Being a U.S. Naval Ship accompanying the U.S. aircraft carrier and associated ships, we were required to carry a *USDAO* or U.S. Defense Attaché Office official. The USDAO's purpose was to monitor the foreign nationals aboard the ship for the Suez Canal transit, such as the Egyptian Pilots and any Egyptian government officials. The USDAO assigned to my ship for the Canal transit was a U.S. Air Force Colonel on assignment to the Middle East, and always dressed inconspicuously in civilian attire. We were almost three quarters of the way through the 20-hour Suez Canal northbound transit and I was on the bridge the entire time. After passing the Great Bitter Lake, the USDAO approached me, as I was perched in the Captain's Chair on the bridge, keeping an eye on all the goings-on, not the least of which was the Suez Canal Pilot. He had departed his post and threw down his prayer rug and started praying toward Mecca. This was happening all the while the ship was transiting the Canal.

The USDAO looked at me and proclaimed, "Excuse me…Master…is it? I don't know what to call you because you are not a REAL Captain (emphasis mine)."

I turned in my roost, looked down at the good Colonel with piercing eyes, and shot back. "You may call me Captain, and as for that nonsense about not being a real Captain, I will only direct you to history. So, tell me, Colonel, who were the first Captains in the first American Navy? Don't bother, I'll answer that. They were the U.S. Merchant Marine, called the Privateers, commissioned by the Continental Congress." With that, I pivoted back to looking ahead.

Needless to say, the USDAO official sheepishly made an about-face and departed the bridge. Evidently, the Colonel must not have been very diplomatic, as he and the Egyptian pilot started arguing toward the end of the Canal transit. Apparently, the USDAO needed to get off the ship with the Egyptian pilot in his pilot boat. The pilot had no use for the USDAO and refused to allow him to board his pilot boat. Meanwhile, as this is going on, the pilot is obviously distracted from his duties and is now getting quite animated. The geographical area was Port Said and the normal 1-kilometer markers which dot the entire length of the Canal were no longer present. Adjacent to the now unmarked section of the Canal at its terminus were shoal areas, one wrong course and the ship would run aground. Obviously with the pilot preoccupied with the USDAO, all my attention turned to the safe navigation of the ship through the Canal terminus into deep water. As the rankling continued between the USDAO and pilot, the USDAO pulled out a diplomatic communique stating he is permitted to use the Egyptian pilot's boat to get off my ship via the pilot boat. Unfortunately for the USDAO, the pilot refused to acquiesce.

At this time, we reached the pilot drop off point, the pilot boat was alongside the ship, waiting for the pilot to disembark, and clear ahead lay the deep blue waters of the Mediterranean Sea. With that, I turned around, and mentioned in a matter of fact tone, "Colonel, if you do not come to some sort of agreement with the pilot, you are welcome to join us for a trip back home. Next stop is Norfolk, Virginia." Low and behold, the USDAO made nice with the Egyptian pilot and was permitted to depart on his pilot boat.

Back onboard SHINNECOCK's saloon. All the seating was of the assigned type in the saloon. At the big round table sat the Captain, the First Officer on his right, and the Chief Engineer on his left. Also sitting at the "adults" table, as it was sometimes referred, was the First Assistant Engineer, the U.S. Navy Commander in charge of the military department, and possibly the Cargo Officer, who is a Chief Mate in his own right, and maybe the Supply officer. I sat at the four-person table adjacent to the Captain's table. My table was for deck officers only, that being the Second Officer, the two Third Officers and any other deck officers we may have aboard from time-to-time. Engineering officers took two four-person tables, U.S. Navy officers at another table, U.S. Navy pilots at yet another, and at the final table sat the staff officers, the Purser, his paramour Peg, the Junior Purser, the Chief Steward, and maybe the Third Steward.

The food was not too bad. Albeit I just arrived, give it a week or two and I am certain I will have complaints. What is that adage? "A mariner is not a mariner unless he is complaining"... yeah, sounds about right. I picked up the menu from the lazy Susan on the table which held all the condiments. The menu sounded as if I were dining in a three Michelin Star restaurant, succulent prime rib au jus with lemon butter, mixed vegetables and whipped whole potatoes, or moist and luscious Tom turkey with cornbread dressing with a wonderful gravy from the juices. Yummy... Wow, that sounded great. I soon found out that the Chief Steward must have been a greeting card writer in a past life, for he could write the most delicious menus, so good, I wish I could have just eaten the menu. For when my meal was placed on my table setting, I had to do a double take. I even took the menu out again to see which one of these wonderful dishes could possibly be hiding in the grub now sitting on my plate. The prime rib looked like a piece of mutton and was way overcooked, the au jus being a mixture of Worcestershire sauce and soy sauce. Oh, and remember the Tom turkey? Yeah, that was turkey roll. What is turkey roll? Well, I had no idea either, but I learned it starts out as all turkey parts, bones included, then its ground up into a paste or slurry, pushed into a form, and there it is—turkey roll. There was no way the gravy was made from the turkey; no, I believe it came straight from a U.S. Military number ten size can, probably canned during the Vietnam War. The food was bad enough; however, it was the ordering process I had to get down.

Here I am again, thinking about the deli on Long Island and the ordering process. In the saloon, when ordering, there were certain key phrases to pass on to the *messmen,* or waiters. It must be noted these messmen are not the brightest bulbs onboard. Think about it, no qualifications necessary, zero; go ahead and fog a mirror, and you got the job. Oh, and any criminal record is a plus. So right away, you're not asking these folks for their recommendations, and all you hope is they washed their hands and don't spit in your food or worse, and there *is* worse.

Starting with the ordering process, one must remember to be quick, be simple, use those key phrases, or all bets are off for what you're getting. For the prime rib with au jus, the ordering goes something like this,

"I'll take the meat in the center, wet, with veggies in a monkey." Translation, "I will have the prime rib only on a plate with au jus, and the vegetables I would like in a small side dish." Sometimes the Messman may get the order, "I'll take a full house." Translation, "I will have everything on the damn menu, I am a big fat pig." I added the damn and big fat pig parts, but who the heck eats everything on the menu? Unbelievably, there are many mariners who do indeed order the full house.

On the SHINNECOCK, we had an *Ordinary Seaman,* the lowest entry-level position in the deck department, right up there with a Messman. He asked for the full house at every meal. He went by the moniker "Big Mac" and he was huge—not muscular, but fat. He was this huge African-American man with the highest pitch voice you could believe. I remember the other seamen yelling at him that he wasn't big, he was just fat. He was a jolly fella though, always smiling; I guess the fat guy is a happy guy.

Now back to the art of ordering. Sometimes I may make this meal order, "I'll take the soup from the bottom." Translation, "Tell the cook to take the ladle all the way to the bottom of the huge pot where all the meat and vegetables have sunk and scoop that up and give it to me." I may get the response, "Cook says he just put it on the fire." Translation, "The cook informed me that he needs to heat up the soup on the stove and it may take awhile, maybe even going beyond the meal hour."

Of course, a menu on the SHINNECOCK wouldn't be complete unless it included items that my mother would threaten to feed me when I was growing up if I misbehaved. For instance, until I arrived onboard the SHINNECOCK, I had no idea Americans ate pigs' knuckles or pigs' feet, frog legs, ham hocks, and pig intestines…for regular meals! When I read those items on the menu, I had to do a double take yet again, and certainly when asked by the messman, I would insist, "No spare parts for me…"

Now one would surmise with such terrible food, everyone would be emaciated; well, not everyone with maybe the exception of Big Mac, but it was not the case. Most of the crew were overweight, some morbidly obese, such as Captain Stone. So how does it happen? Easily, think ice cream, French fries, and burgers. There is always unlimited ice cream 24/7 in each dining facility, the saloon for the officers, the chief's mess for the foreman crew, and the crew mess for the rest of the crew. Ice cream can be either in the form of bars or the like, or soft serve, which we fondly call the "auto-dog," the reason being self-explanatory.

CHAPTER SIX

"During the black years of War, the men of the Merchant Marine did their job with boldness and daring. Six thousand were killed or missing in carrying out their duties. In memory of those men, and in the interest of our Nation, the United States must carry out the bold and daring plan of Franklin D. Roosevelt for a Merchant Marine of the best designed and equipped passenger and cargo ships, manned by the best trained men in the world."

- Harry S. Truman

President of the United States

We got underway about 20:00 for our next commitment, and I looked forward to the chance to sit down and take it all in…my first day as an officer aboard a ship. As such, I proceeded to walk the three decks down from the bridge to my state-room. The bridge was located on the 04-level or four decks above the main deck. My stateroom was again in the forward house on the 01-level port side aft, one deck above the main deck, adjacent to the watertight door to the UNREP deck. When I arrived, I turned the knob on the door to enter. It was dark, so I flipped on the overhead light switch next to the door. Low and behold, as if on cue, a dark-haired woman sits up in my bed from under the covers. I immediately started to apologize profusely, asking forgiveness for such a horrendous mistake as I must have walked into the wrong room. I say my mea culpas while closing the door, as I am mortified for my lack of manners, or so I thought. For as I am about to shut the door, I look up at the embossed sign on the door and it reads, in all caps, "THIRD OFFICER—MR. F. NATALE."

I shook my head for a second in disbelief, and then re-opened the door and said to the woman, "Hey, I believe this is my room—it says it on the door."

The unclothed woman replied matter-of-factly, "Yes, I know. You see, I used to go with Redsen, so when he left, I saw you were kinda cute, so I figured, I'd go with you."

I couldn't possibly believe my ears. Where was I—in some John Waters movie from the 70's, free love and all?

Well, this was not happening, so I replied, "Yeah, ah, that's all fine and nice, but I just got here, as you know, and I don't think it's appropriate and all, and besides, I don't even know your name."

The woman, in a most seductive voice, batting her eyelids with pouting lips, clearly trying her best to convince me, pleads her case, "My name is Bonnie, I'm in the *mildept* (military department). Are you sure you don't want to come in? We could have a great time."

I momentarily lost my collective bearings and started to contemplate her tempting offer before I came to my senses and answered, "While I am flattered, I suppose, I am sure."

Clearly disturbed by the rebuke, Bonnie, now with a harsh voice shot back, "Oh, whatever. It's your loss." Then Bonnie explained she was already fully moved in from her time with Redsen, so it would take a few days to move out.

Now, I was floored. What was this ship, the damn "Love Boat?" I didn't know what to do at this point. The one thing I did know, I wasn't staying in my room tonight. I quickly finished our conversation. "OK, Bonnie, that sounds like a plan. I'll go to the officers' lounge for the night." And with that I left the room.

Bonnie was older than I, maybe twenty-five, fit, not overly attractive, but not hard on the eyes, either. She was a second-class petty officer radioman in our crew, in other words, she was active duty U.S. Navy. I was later told that Bonnie did not so much care for Taylor Redsen, as much as she wanted her own stateroom. The military enlisted personnel had to live in mass berthing areas, which meant all the female active duty lived in one huge room with twenty-five other women in bunks stacked three high. Obviously, there was no real privacy, no real storage for personal effects, clothing, baubles and, most importantly, it was devoid of a private head and shower or bathroom. Evidently, Bonnie moved right in with Redsen, lock, stock, and barrel. In fact, she took every drawer in the dresser, all space in the closet, and of course the private head and shower. Bonnie even placed a decorative mirror adorned with a glass border to keep all her perfumes, lotions, and other feminine scents right smack in the middle of the desk. The head and shower, in the words of my fellas back home, fuhgeddaboudit, she had that looking like something out of a sorority sister's bathroom. I had to ponder, where the hell did Redsen keep all his clothes, toiletries, and such. I guess that was the least of Redsen's concerns.

I made my way up to the forward officers' lounge, which was on the 03-Level in the forward house. There was a vinyl covered three-person *settee,* or sofa, with the requisite stains from many a dirty rear end sitting down for coffee breaks. There was also a small pantry with a sink, coffee machine, small refrigerator, but no microwave. The lounge had an old 27-inch picture tube television opposite from the settee, two lone matching vinyl chairs, and a coffee table to round out the room. Adjacent to the sitting area was a four person permanently mounted game table with a chessboard laminated into the top and two folding chairs. There was one porthole in the lounge with a *dead light* affixed. A deadlight is the blank installed in a porthole so no light can shine out of the room, which may affect the watch team's night vision on the bridge. I sat down on the old settee, kicked off my steel-toed black boots, stretched out, and laid supine, for I had my first watch at midnight, some four hours from this time. I then set my alarm on my chronograph LCD watch for 23:00 and hoped to get some rest.

It appeared I didn't need my alarm after all. At about 23:00, I hear some rustling going on, I look up and it's Captain Jabba the Hutt, bent over in front of the refrigerator assessing his next culinary conquest. Rubbing my eyes, I couldn't believe it. He was in his proper uniform, dirty undershirt and blown our briefs sans any type of shoes, slippers, or foot coverings. As I rise from the settee, the Captain turned and without missing a beat, whilst still hunched over searching for food in the fridge, he barked, "Hey, what? Did Ole Bonnie kick you out tonight?"

I couldn't believe this. Here was the Captain pretty much acknowledging his ship has turned into the floating version of the summer of love without a care in the world.

All I could muster out of my groggy voice was, "Something like that…"

The Captain then turned, now fitted with a plate of what is termed *Hoss-cock*, which is nasty cured meats, several individually wrapped Kraft American Cheese food slices, Wonder bread, French's yellow mustard and two pints of chocolate milk. All this together is considered *Night Lunch,* and is a union requirement. The night lunch is specifically for the midnight watch, as they may have missed the evening meal due to that precious commodity…sleep. The ship's baker is required to put together a plate of the items just mentioned and place one such plate in every lounge onboard. So, in essence, the night lunch, which old Captain Bulldog, the snappy dresser he is, was carrying, was for me! But as he left the lounge with his bounty in hand, he muttered, "Shellie is hungry…" I am thinking, great, no sleep, no way to wash up, I can't even change my underwear, and now, no snack before working for the next four hours. To top it off, who the hell is Shellie? I no sooner found out, Shellie, was a rather short and rotund African-American female Wiper, who was dating?...living with?... shacking up?...whatever the case may be, with the Captain. Now a *Wiper* is the lowest entry-level position in the engine department, akin to the Messman in the steward department or the Ordinary Seaman on deck. The Wiper position is named such due to the fact the original duty of a Wiper was to do just that, wipe up all the oil that splashed off the triple-expansion steam engines of the early 20th century steam ships. Shellie was in her late forties, maybe around the same age as the Captain, and she had ten children. Yes, ten, which she raised all by herself. This was her first job at sea after her kids were out of the house. I guess the old man and Shellie hit it off right away. Rather astonishing, I thought, given Captain Bulldog's racist rants. Maybe it was the veritable "any port in a storm" cliché. In any case, no one was going to say anything. Remember, this was before satellite phones, off ship email, and any way to communicate to the home office the dalliances taking place in the Master's cabin. All in all, the crew loved the fact the Captain had a live-in girlfriend, for it kept him out of the way most of the time. And as mentioned, as he was a moron, this poor excuse for a mariner would do far less damage if he remained in his room – hence where Shellie comes in.

It's about 23:30 and I walk up the one flight *ladderwell*, which is a shipboard term for staircase, and enter the chart room. In the chart-room was the *coffee mess* or coffee station; I poured a hot cup of coffee, added plenty of milk and sugar, and tasted…yuck! It tasted like a combination of mud and battery acid. Coffee on a ship is so important to the mariners. Next to cigarettes, coffee is the only legal vice for the mariner at sea, as all U.S. ships are dry—meaning no alcohol, illegalities notwithstanding. The coffee on the SHINNECOCK was not a brand name—in fact, it had no name. The coffee came in a five-pound green can embossed with a military stock number. I would often say these coffee cans were left over from Vietnam. That, or it was the coffee used to pack drugs to ward off the drug-sniffing dogs. Whatever the origin, the grinds were terrible, stale, dried out, just a real poor blend of coffee. Interestingly enough, the "Old Salts" would drink this coffee black and, moreover, they preferred if it were brewed an hour ago and was cooking off in the pot to give it that "burnt" flavor, so craved by those so inclined. Me, I couldn't handle that swill; I had to dope it up with plenty of milk and sugar, and even with all that, the coffee was still horrible. Oh well, whatever the case, it wasn't like I could run out to a coffee shop, and the word Starbucks wasn't even in the lexicon of the day.

After taking a couple sips of my coffee, I walked out onto the non-air-conditioned bridge. Walking through that door from the cool chart-room to the wheelhouse hit me like a ton of bricks. The clock may have said the middle of the night, but the heat was unbearable and the humidity clammed up my skin within seconds. To top that off, we were steaming with the wind, which meant there was no appreciable breeze of even the hot, muggy air through the open portholes. Next, I was hit by the scent of body order and cigarettes. It's a good thing the seas were calm, or I most certainly would have started vomiting. After my eyes adjusted, I checked the chart, the radar and, most importantly, used my seaman's eye to actually look out from the ship for any *contacts.* "Contacts" are any objects in the water—other ships, fishing boats, buoys, oil rigs, etc. After which, I conducted my turnover with the other Third Officer, Michael. Incidentally, I found it odd that I was given the senior Third Officer watch of midnight to four, and Michael, who had been aboard for months, remained on the junior Third Officer watch of eight to twelve. Historically, this watch is also called the "Captain's Watch" because the Captain would still be awake at this time to stand by and observe the new man. My only guess is that either I was that good, or they thought so little of Michael as a Third Officer. It had to be the latter.

After my turnover and Michael departs the bridge, I introduce myself to my watch team. First was *A/B,* or Able Seaman, Leter. An A/B is an experienced seaman and helmsman and requires several years at sea underway to reach this level. He was a tall and lanky, elderly African-American gent; amazingly, he was eighty years old and yet still working. Leter had coke bottle thick glasses, a closely cropped haircut, and was impeccably dressed in a pressed seaman's uniform consisting of a chambray shirt, navy dungaree pants, steel-toed boots, topped off with a ship's ball cap. As one can imagine, being an A/B for over fifty years, old Leter could steer a ship. He was an outstanding helmsman. On top of that, he was extremely respectful of the officers and very professional. He was an old school U.S. Merchant Mariner if there ever was one. I later learned Leter was a functioning alcoholic who didn't function so well when in port.

A few years later we were sailing together on another ship. We were in the port Charlotte Amalie in St. Thomas, a part of the U.S. Virgin Islands. It should be noted that in the 1980's and 1990's, Charlotte Amalie was known for its criminal activity. In fact, the crew was warned not to venture off the main street or risk the wrath of the local gangs. I was ashore one evening enjoying a libation in one of the many tourist type clubs called the Green House. I departed the club heading for the launch to get back to the ship at anchor. As I was walking out of the Green House, I noticed a man on the ground. As I neared the man, I noticed it was A/B Leter. His face was bloodied, and he was incoherent, essentially highly inebriated. Leter was rambling about being rolled by a gang, and he was drooling profusely from his mouth. As I helped him up and walked him to the launch, I noticed, the one possession he cherished was missing. Leter had a Rolex watch which he purchased in the early 1950's, and he proudly wore it daily. It looks like poor Leter lost his Rolex. Later in my career, I determined you had to be either an alcoholic or a bit insane to go to sea for a living.

Back on the SHINNECOCK, A/B Leter struggled to turn that five-foot telemotor wheel. At lookout was A/B Stanz. He was a thirty-something long haired white guy. A prior U.S. Navy enlisted, he got out and started sailing with MSC. He had a quick wit, would give everyone a nickname, and he had this nervous laugh after everything he said. He reminded me of an aging hipster or heavy metal rocker. He wore his chambray shirt with the tails out; I am figuring he liked to be rebellious, combined with a disheveled look. Stanz, too, was an alcoholic, but instead of being a functional alcoholic, he would rather reek of booze all day and night.

Next, I was introduced to A/B Waddams, who was acting as the Rover. What a name to give the fella who has to walk around the ship at night checking for fires and flooding—*Rover* being short for "roving patrol." I always hated calling him "Rover" on the UHF handheld *radio,* or walkie-talkie. It sounded like a classic movie dog's name. Waddams was in his late sixties or early seventies. You can never tell with merchant seamen, as they age rapidly due to the wonderful life at sea—you know, shuffleboard all day and disco dancing all night…yeah right. He was short in stature with white hair and, just like Leter, he was old school Merchant Marine. Waddams wore his seaman's uniform properly, although nowhere near as neat as Leter, and Waddams was also respectful to the officers. However, Waddams was head-on an alcoholic, neither functioning nor otherwise. I don't think I ever saw him sober. If I did, I sure wouldn't know what to expect. Later on, in my hitch, when the ship was in port, on one of the rare occasions Waddams was not stuttering drunk, I asked if he had a driver's license, so he could take the ship's van to get the mail for the Purser on base. He answered with probably the sentence that summed up his life. Waddams said to me, "Mate, I haven't had a wife or a driver's license since 1969, because at sea you can't drive either of them." How could I possibly respond to those sage words of wisdom? Sadly, at the end of the hitch, we found Waddams dead in a hotel after he'd missed his in port watch. Evidently, when we returned to Norfolk, he went to the local seamen's watering hole, called Nick's, and then took a room at a flophouse across the street, finally succumbing to a heart attack. Yet death wasn't the worst of it for poor Waddams, as he had no real next of kin. When MSC finally found a distant relative, they wouldn't claim old Waddams' body from the morgue. Don't know whatever happened after that—just the fact, he died the way he lived…all alone.

Finally, I met the last man on my watch team, Davis, and he was the Ordinary Seaman of the watch. Davis was a black guy in his early to mid-thirties, also with 10 kids. The other members of the crew called him "Krusty the Clown" or "Soul-Glo." That was all due to his hair, as Davis had a classic 70's Afro hairstyle complete with the pick and everything. Krusty the clown referenced a character on the new TV series the *Simpsons* and Soul-Glo referenced a fictions type of hair gel from the mid-80's Eddie Murphy movie, *Coming to America*. Davis was friendly, always in a good mood, had a high-pitched voice and an infectious laugh. You couldn't help but really like Davis. Best yet, he was one of the lone non-alcoholics onboard, a rarity indeed. The Ordinary Seaman on the watch was required to rotate through all non-officer positions such as helmsman, lookout, and rover, but under instruction until deemed capable. Moreover, when any grunt work appeared on the bridge, such as cleaning, etc., you can bet the A/B's on the watch would hand that task over to the Ordinary Seaman. Worse yet for Davis, since he was the newest and least experienced of all the Ordinary Seaman on the ship, he drew the duties of *Crumb Boss* and the dubious title to match. Now, I thought calling a man "Rover" was bad enough, but calling a man the "Crumb Boss"—that is, the boss of all crumbs, was tough.

I give everyone respect at sea regardless of their job or duty, and that character trait remained with me my entire career, even when I was the Captain. In addition to his normal watch duties, the Crumb Boss had to *soogee* and *swab*, mariner language for clean and mop, the crew's common areas, or crew lounge, and the passageways on the crew decks of the ship. Additionally, the Crumb Boss had to restock the coffee mess on the bridge, meaning he had to resupply with cups, coffee, sugar, milk, etc., in addition to cleaning the bridge as well.

After I met my watch team, I went about my watch duties, one of them being the logbook. At the time, MSC kept a running logbook on 8½ by 14-inch lined sheets with carbon paper sandwiched between a white page and a yellow page. This was far different from the typical U.S. Merchant Marine commercial required logbook, also known as a *rough log*, which, kept by the Watch Officers, was bound, and had just a small section for writing pertinent notes of the watch. In addition, the Master kept a similar logbook, called the *smooth log*. The logbook was sacred, and pages could never be ripped out of the binding or, God forbid, rewritten over and over to the satisfaction of the Master. This was not the case with the MSC logbooks at the time. The daily running log could continue in perpetuity. As long as events continued within that particular 24-hours, the recording would continue page upon page, all the while written in script, or what is now called cursive —and neatness counted! Interestingly enough, if any of the Watch Officers made too many mistakes or didn't write neatly enough, that particular Watch Officer would actually have to rewrite the entire log for that day. In addition, that one officer would even have to rewrite the sections written by the other officers that had no errors, then hunt them down to get them to sign their name. This was mindboggling; I couldn't fathom it—rewriting logbooks? It was drilled into our heads at Ft. Schuyler that no logs can be altered or tampered with, or gasp... rewritten. This apparently did not apply to MSC: in fact, rewriting was so common, it was often the butt of jokes. For those new Third Officers like myself, it took a while to learn the art of MSC logbook writing, and in my case, I was known as "the king of the rewrites." Further, it was the Second Officer who made the determination if a rewrite was necessary. Ultimately, the Master would approve the logs, but the Second Officer wouldn't let anything but perfect logs make it to the Captain's desk. At the end of the voyage, the Second Officer would separate the copies from the originals, then apply a two-hole punch to the top and metal tabs to bind all the pages together. The original would go to MSC and the copy to remain on the ship. Certainly not how I was trained in the art of logbook keeping. Just an aside, I later, by chance, found out where the bound copies of all the ships' logs wind up at MSC. Back at MOTBY in Building 42, on the fourth floor, the halls were lined with metal file cabinets. One day when I was stuck in the purgatory of Building 42, I happened to open one of the drawers on a lone filing cabinet in the hallway just outside the entrance to the famed mariners' lounge. Interestingly enough, it was unlocked, but sure enough, I found reams and reams of bound ships' logs.

I was preparing to start the midnight log entry for the SHINNECOCK, and incidentally it would be my first logbook entry in my career. I didn't have the foggiest idea where to start, so I figured I would just look at the previous night's midnight entry to mimic. However, before I could put pen to logbook paper, A/B Stanz informed me of a contact off to the port side, a *loom* he called it, which was short for "luminous." Simply put, this meant there was something lighting up just below the horizon, but he could not ascertain if it were a ship or something else. If indeed a ship, a loom is normally visible prior to the contact ship's actual lights coming into view. This is due to several factors, including the curvature of the earth and the ship's lights luminous range characteristics. I immediately dropped the log, walked out to the port bridge wing, raised my binoculars to look, then pointed the alidade on the gyro repeater at the loom. After a couple of minutes, I checked the alidade and, sure enough, the loom, which was not clearly identified as a ship at the time, had a left bearing drift. This meant the contact was not a risk of collision; I could continue on my course and speed while monitoring the contact.

Feeling pretty good about myself, I walked into the bridge through the port blast re-enforced watertight door, with my head held high. Unfortunately, I did not get to bask in my fine watch standing skills, as I noticed, through the black of the bridge with just the reflection of the red lights on all the equipment, a rather large figure at the chart table. As I approached, the figure was clearly one of the female varieties, but this time, she was tall, in fact, taller than me, but bottom heavy with large hips, which did not fit well in her uniform. I quickly announced, "Excuse me, excuse me, can I help you?"

The female figure turned to me and I could see her red hair and very light complexion, that and the fact that she looked young, very young. I also noted her Navy uniform with nothing on the sleeve in the way of rank, clearly visible. Then she began to speak with the hardest Deep South drawl I had ever heard, "Oh, I wuz fixin' to start the log."

I shot back, "What log? And what—you're fixing something?" Now looking at her, she was clearly confused, almost befuddled, for this was probably the biggest conundrum she had faced aboard SHINNECOCK, sarcasm emphasized.

She retorted, "I always wrote the log for Redsen, so here I am."

I thanked her and ushered her away. Her name was Jane Smithers, but everyone called her "Big Red," and she was a seaman in the Navy department aboard the ship assigned to the signal bridge, as she was *striking*, or learning to become a signalman. A Navy signalman, now long since gone, would use semaphore and flashing lights to send messages to other ships in the battle group. Additionally, the signalmen would handle all the *flag hoists*, or signal flags, which flew from the yardarms on the main mast, and finally, they acted as lookouts with their super powerful twenty-power Mark 3 MOD 0 permanently fixed binoculars, or *Big Eyes*, as they were referred. The signalmen were stationed on the signal bridge, or flying bridge, that is one deck above the actual navigation bridge, or wheelhouse. Big Red, just recently eighteen, was the youngest on the SHINNECOCK, and this was her first trip out of her one traffic light town of Lummock, Texas.

After Jane Smithers departed the bridge and returned to signal bridge, I started to put pen to paper and commence writing my midnight log entry. Just like that, the wonderful serene sound of the ship running through the water was breached, "Aren't you going to go up and diddle Big Red?" Shocked, I turned; it was Leter, at the helm, in his half-drunken stupor, mumbling to me.

"What are you saying?"

Leter then replied as if it was normal, "Mate, Sir, Mr. Redsen, would go up to the signal bridge and play around with Big Red, and he told us to call him if we saw any contacts or if the phone rang." Now I had that "ah-ha" moment, for now I understood what Redsen meant when he said I would love this ship. Damn Redsen has got a harem, I thought. He's got Bonnie down in his stateroom waiting for him and Big Red on the signal bridge. How the hell did he keep up and, moreover, keep each of them from knowing what was going on with the other girl. I knew this guy was a player, but I had no idea he was in the major leagues. Just the more reason to stay away from those two. Redsen was slimy to the core.

With that, I said to Leter, "Well, Leter, I cannot speak for Mr. Redsen, but for me, this is my job and I'll keep it professional."

He replied, "OK, Mate, Sir, you're old school for a young officer." And that was it, from then on Big Red would only come down to the bridge to report a contact, report a signal she received, or tell me she is fixing to go eat.

Although I couldn't help myself, every time she said she was "fixin'" to go wherever, I would always ask, "Why…is it broken?" She never did understand my humor in that response; so much so, she would then go on to explain at great length where, in fact, where she would be going and what she would be doing. Meanwhile, Leter, Stanz, and Waddams would chuckle at Big Red missing the humor.

I started writing the midnight log in script…

"Vessel underway in accordance with US Navy and MSC operational orders number (fill in), with CAPT Stone, Master, in Command, 14 licensed MSC officers, 6 MSC Staff officers, 70 MSC crew, 2 USN officers, 26 USN enlisted, 6 USN pilots, 22 USN enlisted air detachment, and 2 passengers for a total of 149 souls aboard. Vessel is on course 205 degrees per gyrocompass, 189 per magnetic Enroute to UNREP with USS BOWEN FF-1080. Engine room manned by third assistant engineer Jones as the watch engineer, with an unlicensed junior engineer Robinson, and an oiler Strong; boiler room manned by third engineer Mosses with fireman Sweet on duty. Both engines rung up full ahead for 95 RPM with boilers number 2 and 3 online to make good 20 knots. Ship's service steam turbine generators SSTG's number 1,2, and 3 online providing hotel services. Wet fire main online with fire pump number 1 online and emergency fire pump number 3 providing back up. All running lights are burning bright and vessel is navigating via celestial, radio, and electronic navigation, with Raytheon Ray-Cas X-band Radar assisting with collision avoidance. Third Officer Frank Natale watch officer with A/B Leter, A/B Stanz, and A/B Waddams rotating at helm, lookout, and rover, O/S Davis under instruction and acting as crumb

> ***boss. US Navy Seaman Smithers on watch as signalman..."***

That is just the start of the typical daily log; from that point on I would have to add anything and everything that happened to include course changes, engine changes, alarms, radio messages, notification of the Master or any other officers coming to the bridge in an official capacity, etc. Writing this narrative seems bad enough, but that is nothing compared to the first log entry of the New Year. Take this exact log entry and make every sentence rhyme like a poem in iambic pentameter! It was an old tradition that would not die.

CHAPTER SEVEN

"Since I became the Chairman of the Joint Chiefs of Staff, I have to appreciate first-hand why our Merchant Marine has long been called our Nation's fourth arm of defense. The American Seafarer provided an essential service to the well-being of the Nation as was demonstrated so clearly during Operation Desert Shield and Desert Storm...."

- General Colin Powell

Chairman of the Joints Chief of Staff

Not soon after I arrived, I met the Cargo Officer, or *Cargo Mate*. The Cargo Mate is normally a Chief Mate and a department head in charge of all the cargo, cargo gear, and the cargo deck gang, which includes a Cargo Boatswain, or Bosun, and he normally answers directly to the Master, both operationally and administratively. However, there are occasions in which the Cargo

Mate is actually a Second Mate, and, in such cases, he does not head an independent department, rather he falls under the Chief Mate or First Officer in the deck department. Onboard the SHINNECOCK, this was the exact case. Maybe due to the fact no one wanted the ship or the lack of deck officers, the Cargo Mate on SHINNECOCK started with MSC two years prior to me as a Third Officer. His name interestingly enough was Lawrence Arthur Stone and he went by his initials L.A.S. pronounced "LAZ" for short. In a shocking coincidence, he and the Captain shared the same surname. They claimed they were not related, but they were both from Maine. LAS seemed quite odd, but then he was from Maine and all.

At this point, I must mention a bit of information in regard to the mariners from Maine. It is well known; Maine has a long and proud history of brave and able seafarers, mostly stalwart fishermen, as is the same throughout all of New England. However, the mariners from Maine take pride in the fact they are a little different than most others, different in an idiocentric sense. They even refer to themselves as "Maniacs." I will give them this accolade,: Maine mariners, specifically, graduates of Maine Maritime Academy in Casteen, are overall the finest marine engineers, bar none. That being said, I must disclose, some of these engineers are not from the State of Maine, but rather only attended Maine Maritime Academy in Casteen. As such, they may be exempted from the oddities of the native Maine seafarers. The Maniacs, as they again refer to themselves, are generally cheap. Not frugal, but cheap; these guys probably still have the money they received as gifts after their first Holy Communion. Most of the Maine mariners have large sums of cash, but not in a bank, nope, because they don't really trust the government. They also possess a biting sense of humor and a lack of culture or refinement. When the Maine mariners go out to town when the ship is in port, many wear their same work clothes…stains and all.

I once sailed with a very competent and genuine engineer from Maine, Benny Lankforth. He was one of the nicest guys you would ever meet. However, personal hygiene, or lack thereof, which was another common Maniac trait, was not Benny's strong suit. He was so filthy and nasty, the *BR*, or Bedroom Steward, refused to clean his room, a privilege provided to all officers on the ships. I remember when I was First Officer, Benny complained to the Captain of the fact the BR spurned tending to his stateroom. The Captain on that ship, who incidentally was both my mentor and dear friend, and in no way resembled any of the characteristics of Stone, informed Benny that he ordered the BR not to clean his room. Benny was incredulous, so the Good Captain took a tour of Benny's room and, after digging through the layers of nasty dirty clothes and funky undergarments, Benny got the point.

Warnings such as this to his poor personal hygiene, or *PPH* as I call it, fell on Benny's deaf ears. Years later when I was the Master of a particular ship and the crew was staying in apartments due to the ship being in drydock, I received a concerned call from the apartment complex managing company. Evidently, when the management company had to enter Benny's room, they found ten, five-gallon jerry jugs filled with diesel fuel. Not to be outdone, in the living room, on a white sheet, they found a small block Chevy engine in a state of rebuild—right there in the living room! When I spoke to Benny, he commented that he found a great price on diesel fuel for his truck about an hour away, so he filled jerry jugs to use later. A fire hazard and putting the complex at risk did not even phase him. I truly believe he did not even consider that fact. As for the rebuilding of the engine in the living room, well, he and a Third Engineer, also by chance from Maine, were rebuilding his car engine. I thought, if this is how he treats his company-provided apartment, I couldn't imagine the state of disarray in his Thomaston, Maine home. However, it bears repeating, these were two of the most technically competent and knowledgeable marine engineers. I would take the idiosyncrasies and oddities any day to have these engineers on my ship.

Case in point, I was Master on another ship, a new-build this time, and Benny was the Cargo Engineer. The sliding door to the bridge wing integrated door toggle-handle, latch, and lock mechanism was not functioning. I, of course, requested Benny to the bridge. After he arrived, I showed him the issue and he told me not to worry, he would take care of it. A week later, I was on the bridge and happened to notice the sliding door handle, latch, lock mechanism. It looked brand new! Now there was no way it could be new, as we did not order a new part and, beside the fact, we had been underway at sea the entire time. Sure enough, I tested the door mechanism out, and it worked flawlessly. In fact, the Benny repair operated more efficiently than the other bridge wing door, which had its factory mechanism installed. I had to know how Benny did it. I called Benny to the bridge and said, "Benny, the latching locking handle mechanism looks unbelievable and works flawlessly, how could you have done that out here?"

Benny smiled and proudly retorted, "Well Captain, it was not too difficult. I just had to fabricate every part, using our milling machine, lathe, and other fabrication equipment."

Flabbergasted, with my jaw hanging open, I shot back, "Benny, you made every single part?"

Benny dutifully answered, "Yes sir, every part."

Now going through my mind was the unimaginable amount of overtime this repair was going to cost my budget. But before, I could get a word out, Benny continued, "Captain, it's gonna cost you, though. I have like forty hours into the job."

I was speechless. That would cost more than buying an entire new sliding door with the latch mechanism already installed. But, who am I to argue? I asked Benny to repair the door and I never asked how much overtime it would incur. I would know better for next time. However, the fact remained, Benny and the Maine engineers could fix anything, even if they had to fabricate the parts in the middle of the ocean, and this was before 3-D printers were even in our language.

In another Maine mariner case, I had the pleasure of sailing with a particular A/B from Maine who would rock side to side as he was standing behind the wheel, steering the ship. He looked as if he were afflicted with some mental disorder, rocking continuously – side to side. He hated women and refused to work for female deck officers, saying, "I ain't working for no split tail." When this A/B got on a ship, he would not leave the ship for over a year. When I mean he would not leave the ship, I mean he would not even get off the ship to stand on the pier for over a year. He wasn't a drunk, so in my hypothesis, he must have been insane. I'd say that was a good estimation.

Then there was a Third Officer from Maine, Bob Beaner. We called this guy "Bouncing Bob." Instead of rocking port and starboard as the A/B from Maine had done, Bouncing Bob would stand at the window looking out, grab onto the handrail and bounce forward and back, over and over, like some crazed witch doctor. I don't know, maybe there is a balancing problem or inner ear issue with the Maine seafarers. What are the chances I would run into not one, but two Maniacs who are bouncing and bobbing? This is the stuff that cannot be fabricated.

In any case, LAS was tall, about six-foot, five-inches and lanky, with a very deep voice and a nervous laugh after everything he said. Oh, and he possessed that wonderful trait of poor personal hygiene, or PPH. The deck gang even had a name for LAS… "Stinky." They would slip bars of soap in his room to give him a hint…all to no avail. LAS' BR even put baby powder in his shower stall to see how many days LAS would go without even showering. The BR said one time he went an entire week sans shower. What was more troubling was the fact he was a graduate of the federal maritime academy at Kings Point. I would have thought he should have learned, at the very least, to shower whilst a midshipman at the Academy. LAS was quite full of himself as well, and the fact he not only shared the same last name with Captain Bulldog, and that they were both from Maine, made for quite a bit of conceit on the part of this sycophant. I remember LAS would stand with a foot on the lower railing, continuously drinking Diet Coke, and he had a perpetual Diet Coke in his hands at all times, at that.

I can attest to the fact that the A/B's didn't appreciate Stinky, and to say he was an ass is being kind. Recall, in the chartroom was located the coffee mess, or coffee station. To save paper cups and trees, I guess, we all had ceramic mugs with our names affixed with the old-style embossing tape. One day on watch, I stuck my head into the chart room looking for the Crumb Boss and I see another A/B coming out of the head with the LAS' coffee mug in hand. I looked more intensely, and it appeared he was drying the mug, and then he walked back to the coffee station and hung LAS' mug up on its hook. I thought this was odd. Why would anyone take LAS' cup into the head?

At this point, I made that critical error that I would learn never to repeat: I asked the question. I asked the A/B what he was doing with LAS' coffee mug. "A/B, what's going on with the Cargo Mate's mug?"

The A/B coyly replied, "Do you really want to know, Mate?" Uh oh, here was my chance to back out and have plausible deniability. But again, I was still rather new to the world of the American Merchant Seamen. I couldn't help myself. I had to know.

"Yeah, sure."

The A/B then began in the most matter-of-fact dialogue you could imagine, as if he was reading stereo assembly instructions. "You see, Mate, every day one of us takes ole' Stinky's mug into the head, we then piss in it and brush our junk all over it for good measure. Then we dry it out and hang it up for him."

I shot back in my best nonchalant way, "OK, well, I am sure he deserves it." Right then and there, I vowed to never leave my mug out of my sight for the rest of my career. Better yet, I vowed to always treat the unlicensed crew with kid gloves.

No sooner did I close the door to the chart room and walk back on the bridge, but I turned around and there was LAS standing there, coffee mug in hand, sipping away, none the wiser of the little extra protein in his java. Ironically, LAS had been drinking with his piss cup for months. Well, I understand urine is, in fact, sterile. I never did think about saying anything to him, or certainly not to the A/Bs to distract from their daily "Cargo Mate coffee cup duties."

The Chief Engineer, Stan Nowak, was in his late fifties, small in stature, and a tad rotund. He had the typical round Polish-American facial features, short black hair, and was a raging alcoholic, which at this point in my residence aboard the SHINNECOCK, I was learning was par the course on the ships. I rarely ever saw or even said two words to the Chief, and from my understanding, he rarely perused the engine room, which was his charge. This was to the chagrin of the other engineering officers. Although, when he did speak, it was usually in a gruff tone with a condescending or critical bent. As mentioned, he was a hard-core alcoholic, and the only real interaction we had in my tenure aboard occurred one night whilst we were in port at Naval Station Rodman in Panama, making our weekly resupply port call.

I was standing the midnight to eight AM in port watch with my usual cast of characters, Leter, Stanz, Waddams, and Davis. Now, when a ship is in port, the gangway from the ship to pier may be either provided by the port or the ship may use its installed accommodation ladder. In either case, when the gangway is on the pier, by law, there must be a huge net slung underneath from the point where the gangway meets the side of the ship all the way down to the pier. This net, as I was taught at Ft. Schuyler, was required in the event someone would fall off the gangway when boarding the ship. However, in all honesty, no one ever really believed this net would actually be used for such, or even if it were, would ever actually save someone. Rather, everyone figured the net was in place for the proverbial check in the box, sort of like, when clothes labels have “Dry Clean Only” affixed, but no one pays attention, and throws it in the washing machine, anyway.

So here I am standing at the gangway area about 01:00 with my watch team and stumbling up to the top of the gangway appears the little Chief Engineer. When he set foot at the top step, right before he would step off the gangway onto the ship proper, he stopped, slurred a “Hi” in a low voice, and then he started to sway to balance himself, as if on a balance beam. It was clear the Chief went beyond his own ten-drink limit, was essentially incoherent and could barely remain erect. As if in slow motion replay, the Chief swayed back and forth, one time, two times, three times.... Then...kerplunk, he fell right over off the gangway! Leter and I stood frozen in disbelief. Could this really have happened? Did the Chief just fall off the gangway? After what seemed like an eternity, but was probably seconds in real time, the two of us ran to the side of the ship and started looking down. Low and behold, the little Chief fell right into the net! It was like a circus act that falls off the trapeze wire into the net. We watched Nowak roll out of the net right onto the pier – a perfect 10! And he's OK, too! But wait, without missing a beat, the Chief hopped on his feet and stumbled back up the gangway, albeit with a little more caution, and stepped off the gangway onto the ship, mumbled "Good Night," and off he went. Meanwhile, we are standing there with our mouths wide open, barely believing what we just witnessed.

The SHINNECOCK had two Boatswains, or Bosuns, in our jargon. We had a Ship's Bosun, who was akin to a foreman for the deck gang, and tended to all the deck structures, maintenance, repair, marlinespike seamanship and the like, answering directly to the Chief Mate. The UNREP Bosun was responsible for all the underway replenishment rigs, all associated equipage, all cargo handling—and reported to the Cargo Mate. Our two bosuns were both former U.S. Marines during Vietnam, but they couldn't stand each other.

The Ship's Bosun, Jason Pickle, was a master seaman and an intellectual. In fact, years later he would go on to be an adjunct professor at a small New England liberal arts college. That's quite a change, going from a Ship's Bosun to a college classroom. Bosun Pickle had no use whatsoever for Third Officers, and he barely had a use for any mate less than a Chief Mate. Even then, the Chief Mate would have to be extremely competent and with years of experience. Pickle was tall, maybe six-foot five, but not scrawny like the Cargo Mate; rather, he was built—with snow white hair, clean shaven and he stood statue tall. He walked with purpose, always looking directly ahead. Most notably, he did not tolerate incompetence from either his men or the officers. If Bosun Pickle sensed a weak officer, that poor bastard was finished. Bosun Pickle would shred him to pieces with his quick wit and genius. But he would always disarm in a way that did not reflect disrespect, but clearly dispensed with such an uncouth officer. Interestingly enough, Bosun Pickle ran an unauthorized and anonymous underground newsletter, which was more desirable by the rank and file than the official MSC fish wrap. Unbelievably, he was right most of the time, to the disgruntlement of those in charge at MSC. What was more astonishing, Pickle put this newsletter out in the age before the internet, email, or fax. Like clockwork, every month, the newsletter would work its way around the MSC fleet. Many a NIS agent, the precursor to NCIS, would stop for a chat with Bosun Pickle. But he would outsmart them and never once was he proven to be behind the newsletter, even though everyone knew the truth.

The UNREP, or Cargo Bosun, Alejandro Ramirez, was also a master seaman, maybe the best seaman in the strictest sense of the word. In regard to cargo and UNREP, Ramirez had no equal. On top of that, Bosun Ramirez was a workaholic, with unbounded energy and drive, and he possessed a loyalty to his Chief Mate not often seen. Any Chief Mate or Master would be well served to have Bosun Ramirez running the UNREP rigs and handling the cargo. He and I started a professional relationship that would span 25 years. During my years as Cargo Mate or Chief Mate or even as Master, if I were taking out a new class of ships, or what-have-you, I would always bring Bosun Ramirez with me. I knew to surround myself with the best. He and I were both respectful of each other, even after the 25 years I was Captain to him, and he was Bosun to me.

Ramirez's seamanship prowess would surface at critical times. Once such incident occurred years later, when I was Chief Mate on a Fast Combat Stores ship. We were conducting replenishment operations with the aircraft carrier USS GEORGE WASHINGTON CVN-75 at a furious pace. In fact, that particular UNREP would go on to set records and milestones not since replicated. In any case, one of the wire rope cargo slings parted, stopping the ability to send cargo at one entire station. To change out that particular fixed sling would have taken precious time. Not to worry, Bosun Ramirez appeared from out of nowhere and deftly took the broken sling and with the skill of a surgeon fashioned a *Molly Hogan* and *Flemish*. Next thing everyone knew, the rig was back up and running as if nothing happened. Seasoned seamen looked on in awe as Ramirez performed his handiwork. School was most certainly in, and the headmaster was the Bosun.

Bosun Ramirez, was medium height, but built, and very strong, like Samson from the Bible. He was a proud *Boricuan*, which translates into "Brave and noble lord of Puerto Rico," but it really means native Puerto Rican. He could have a hot Latin temper at times, but always when the men wouldn't work hard enough. Although 100% Boricuan, Bosun Ramirez had what looked like some Asian features, especially his eyes. So much so, he had a nickname by the men—"China" or "Bosun China." It didn't seem to bother him. I should mention Bosun Ramirez was an old school American Merchant Marine Bosun. Many a time, when a Chief Mate had a malcontent for a seaman, he would have Bosun Ramirez take him to the Bosun locker to instill some respect and work ethic in the discontented mariner. For some reason, after such a meeting, that crewman would be the picture of efficiency and cooperation, never to utter a peep of unhappiness.

Bosun Ramirez did possess some rather humorous qualities. For instance, since English was his second language, he would often mangle the name of certain equipment. These were not to the degree of full-blown malapropisms, but interesting and comical. The men even called these mispronounced words "Bosun China-isms." Examples include referring to the "RHIB" pronounced "RIB" with the "H" silent. *RHIB* was an acronym for Rigid Hull Inflatable Boat. However, Bosun Ramirez would refer to this boat as the "RIG" boat rather than "RIB" boat. Another example referred to shrink wrap, which the cargo teams would use to secure loose items on a pallet of cargo. The Bosun would ask for "Shrimp-Shrap."

My assigned BR, which, as mentioned, is the term for the officer's Bedroom Steward, bears mentioning as well. Essentially, this is an entry-level position similar to the Ordinary Seaman, Crumb Boss, or Wiper, except the BR resides in the Steward's department. My BR onboard, Nancy Greenleaf, was an older African-American lady, who seemed a bit out of place. She was in her late fifties and kept herself very well-coiffed. Years later, Nancy would try lawsuit after lawsuit to become a junior purser, like Peg. However, I had no idea at the time that this woman was just plain nuts. My old adage again proved true, recall going to sea, you are either an alcoholic or insane. One day I caught Nancy with a tape measure, mapping out each officer's room, regardless of the fact each room had the same exact measurements. When I asked what she was doing, Nancy informed me she was documenting the square footage of work she is required to perform. OK, that sounded insane, but who am I to judge? And besides, she treated me well and did a nice job. I guess it didn't hurt that I took my father's sage advice from the get-go. My dad told me to make sure I tip the BR every time I get paid. Therefore, every two weeks like clockwork, I left $20 for my BR Nancy. Evidently, I was the only officer who did such.

Another time, I ran into Nancy in the passageway and she proceeds to tell me she was married to Flip Wilson, the 1970's comedian with the catchphrase, "The devil made me do it!" Well, I remember watching *The Flip Wilson Show* so, of course, I didn't believe a word Nancy was uttering. Remember she is...insane. I didn't learn to just walk away when I saw crazy, I actually engaged her in a conversation over Flip Wilson. I then proceeded to ask Nancy, "If you were really married to Flip Wilson, what was his real first name?"

"Flip," she answered in deadpan style.

Now I knew she was off her rocker. Knowing I had to exit lunacy, I quickly shot back, "You don't say." Then I turned and walked away. I knew I shouldn't have engaged in that diatribe.

Shockingly that is not the best of Nancy the BR. No, the incident with my BR that takes top prize centered upon the head or, more specifically, cleaning the commode or toilet bowl in my stateroom. After about my third or fourth watch, I was sitting at my desk in my stateroom. It was about 16:00 and Nancy had just entered to start cleaning my room. I didn't think much of it as she started in my head and shower. After what seemed like an inordinate amount of time in my bath, I thought I needed to check on Nancy—after all she wasn't working with a full deck. As I walked over to my head, I saw Nancy cleaning my toilet with the toilet brush and bowl cleaner. I thought, OK, that seems normal. I then started to turn to go back to my desk, and with that what I caught out of the corner of my eye caused my jaw to drop. Nancy had finished with my toilet bowl and was starting to clean my sink with the same toilet bowl brush and toilet cleaner!

"What are you doing?" I yelled.

Nancy shot back, "What the hell do you think I am doing; I'm cleaning your sink."

"Nancy, toilet bowl brush and cleaner for the toilet bowl, not the sink where I wash my face and brush my teeth!"

She quipped, "Well, what's the difference anyway"?

I couldn't resist any longer. "The difference is I don't want toilet bowl crap in my mouth or on my toothbrush, not to mention the cleaner is rather caustic."

Nancy finally got the point but had to have the last word. "OK, OK, but I have been doing it all along for all the officers and no one has said anything before." I might as well have stuck my head in the bowl every morning to wash my face. I learned my lesson, from then on: whenever my BR would come to service my stateroom, I would always leave. I did that from that day forward for my entire career. I figured what I don't know won't hurt me. I resolved the fact that it's far better I don't know. Had I not known of Nancy's toilet-to-sink cleaning technique, I would be no different than all the other officers… that being that the officers on the SHINNECOCK were oblivious to the fact that they all had toilet mouth syndrome. And not to forget, I tipped Nancy $20 every two weeks!

The 1st Assistant Engineer or, more colloquially, the "1st Engineer" or just "the 1st," Ibrahim Joof, was a hawsepiper who started as a Wiper and was originally from Senegal, Africa. Joof was in his mid-thirties, stood medium height, but thin—almost emaciated thin. He had a ruddy and dark complexion with short curly hair. He always wore his blue ship-issued coveralls and spoke with somewhat of a French accent.

I didn't have much interaction with Joof, but one time was quite memorable. We were in port at Naval Station Rodman conducting our weekly resupply for the eventual replenishment to the fleet. This was the first port visit since I signed aboard the SHINNECOCK. At that time, it was common practice that the ship would only be given two land phone lines with one connected from the pier to the watch station at the gangway phone on the ship; and the other from the pier to the Captain's office on the ship. We did not even have the technical capability to transfer any calls from that phone to a particular ship office or stateroom phone. As such, anyone receiving a phone call would have to physically take the call at the gangway. It was about lunchtime, and I happened to be standing by at the gangway so old Leter could grab a bite to eat. With that, I noticed Joof walking past me and heading down the gangway. However, he was not alone, as he had a small, young bleached blond lady in tow. I should mention, since MSC was infamous for keeping a mariner away from home for long periods of time, many a wife would meet the ship in certain ports to visit, especially if the ship were going to be in port for more than a few days. Again, being new to MSC, and new to the philandering of the typical mariner, I was not aware of the "protocol" for incoming personal phone calls. With that, the phone rang, I picked it up, and a female voice on the other end asked, "Hello, I am looking for 1st Engineer Joof." Almost instantly, as I had just seen him and his lady go ashore for lunch, I pleasantly responded, "Oh, yes, I just saw him go ashore with his wife."

After a painful silence, the woman barked back to me, "What do you mean his wife…I AM HIS WIFE." After hearing this, I felt a lump in my throat; I was thinking, what had I done? I quickly tried to regroup.

"Oh, I'm sorry, Ma'am, I must have been mistaken. I am rather new aboard."

The wife was not buying it for one second, and quipped, "No, no, no, you were right the first time. Well you tell that bastard, when he gets off the ship on vacation, not to come home." And with that she hung up the phone.

One may think the story would end at this point, but that was not the case, for that very same day, Joof approached me in a huff. "What the hell did you tell my wife? Do you know she is talking divorce, and she's locked me out of the bank account?"

I turned and looked at him in the eye, I was furious; he was blaming me for his dalliances with the young blonde. I shot back, "Look, 1st, how am I to know you are messing around behind your wife. If you should be angry with anyone, look in the mirror. It's not my job to keep up with your lies."

He retorted right back, "Yeah, let me give you some advice, Third Mate. When someone calls for anyone on the ship, just take a message. You have no idea the doghouse you put me in." Then he walked away.

As it turned out, the young blonde was a 19-year-old radioman from the SHINNECOCK's military department. I guess I should have known better, albeit being aboard the "Love Boat" SHINNECOCK, but the thought of it was gross and bordering on lecherous. As it turned out, Joof's wife did eventually divorce him, but he wound up marrying again and, like a bad penny, I would sail with him again and again throughout my career.

On another occasion sailing with Joof, this time I was the First Officer on a ship departing a shipyard and heading back to homeport. For the benefit of the crew, we load all the crewmember cars aboard so they'll have their cars when we arrive at homeport. The only catch is that each crewmember desiring this service must sign a waiver, indemnifying the ship, crew, or the government in the event the car is damaged or worse. Another wrinkle in this unique service is the fact it must be performed outside of normal working hours so as not to project conflict of interest. And finally, the cars must be loaded using the ship's own equipment and manpower. When it came time to load 1st Joof's car, a late model Corvette with extensive body additions, the lifting slings crushed his extra body moldings. Joof went absolutely crazy and started yelling and screaming at the Bosun and me. The fact his car had the after-market moldings that made it impossible for the lifting slings to properly cradle the car meant nothing to him. After that incident, I would sail with Joof many more times until one day I found him dead in his stateroom.

After about a week onboard the SHINNECOCK, I learn the 2nd Assistant Engineer, referred to as the "2nd," Bill Rinehart, holds a private weekly party, ship's schedule permitting, of course, in his stateroom—very hush-hush and all. Recall the engineering officers lived in the after house, far away from the Captain, the Chief Mate, and the U.S. Navy Department's officers. Bill hailed from New England and was a Massachusetts Maritime Academy graduate some five years earlier. He was on the shorter side, but he had a James Dean look and you could see he liked to party and loved the ladies. Interestingly enough, Bill was linked to Big Red—in the biblical sense. He was a very competent engineer, and as the 2nd, Bill was responsible for the steam boilers and the fuel. Captain Bulldog would refer to him as "Slick," which I am certain pertained to his womanizing—not oil, as in the fuel.

Bill notified me to come to his room after midnight, but I didn't know how I would do that since I had the watch from midnight to four AM. Bill smiled and told me not to worry. So, I didn't think much of it and went about my day. The next time I went to watch, everything went normal, and normal is good when on watch. In fact, boring with no excitement while serving as Watch Officer on the bridge is the optimal type of watch. Standing watch as a deck officer in the American Merchant Marine is 99% boredom coupled with 1% sheer terror. It is that 1% I wanted to avoid. At about 01:00, the chartroom door opened up and in walked the Second Mate, Matt. He said he was coming up early for his watch. Now he would normally relieve me at 04:00, but this is three hours earlier, so at first, I was a bit perplexed, and then it hit me. This was the wink and a nod that Bill was talking about when I informed him I had watch during his…err…get together.

So, I conducted my turnover with Matt as if it was a normal watch turnover; nothing else is mentioned. I left the bridge and I headed straight aft to Bill's stateroom. When I got to the door, I could clearly hear the music, and most notably, female voices. I stood in front of the door thinking, "What the hell am I doing? Maybe I should just go back to my stateroom and go to sleep. I've only been here a week, and already I am about to get involved in something most likely nefarious." I knocked on the door and I was ushered into Bill's stateroom. His room appeared as if it were converted into a makeshift nightclub. He had installed black lighting and a mirrored disco ball. Over in the corner was a beautiful handcrafted wooden bar, which I later learned was custom-built by Bosun Pickle. There must have been two dozen people crammed into the room. Obviously, Bill, the host, was there, but also, two 3rd Assistant Engineers or "3rds," the Chief Steward, the Electrician, the Cargo Engineer, two A/B's who I didn't know, the Cargo Mate, and the rest—fifteen or so military department and helicopter detachment female Navy enlisted. Of those were, of course, Big Red and Amy, the first girl I laid my eyes on when the SHINNECOCK was arriving while I was standing on the pier. Before I knew it, I had a drink in my hand. Not a beer, which I would have figured, rather a rock glass with single malt scotch whiskey. I noticed this right away; everyone was drinking high balls and throwing back shots. OK, so I am now thinking, "Well, I did it now; I am drinking on the ship…the antithesis of what I was taught." But then I thought, what the hell, this ship is so damned unconventional and irreverent, when in Rome, do as the Romans do.

The music was eighties pop: Madonna, Tears for Fears, Huey Lewis and the News, Hall and Oates, and the like. Bill took me aside and asked me what I thought, especially about all the military department girls. Then he went through them one-by-one, identifying each one's paramour. Then he arrived at Amy, and Bill said the oddest thing to me. "Of course, you've heard about Amy. She's the one everyone wants to go out with." I nodded in the affirmative. "Her last beau aboard was the old Cargo Mate, but he left about three months ago, and she's been single ever since." Again, I nodded, but said nothing. However, Bill wouldn't stop. "All the crew want her, you know, but she has a policy, no khaki, no crackie." Now, I was a bit thrown off, but later decoded Bill's misogynistic phrase—in other words, Amy only dated officers, to the irritation of the crew.

Amy was older than I, at twenty-seven to my twenty-two; she was the axiomatic older woman in every sense of the word. She was a very attractive five-foot three inches with brown flowing hair, when it wasn't up, as required by her Navy uniform. She had Polish or Eastern European facial features with a nice shape, except her hips and butt. I must make mention of the fact that Kim Kardashian had not even been born and Jennifer Lopez was still an unknown dancer. As such, the age of the "big bootie," for lack of other words, was not mainstream. For me and my Long Island roots, those female attributes were not the highest on the list of most desirable at the time. However, the deck gang of A/Bs and O/S's, mostly from L.A., meaning "Lower Alabama," were African-American, and they always spoke of Amy's abundant rear or, as they called them, baby-making hips. I think she knew she was driving the deck gang crazy, because when she would walk across the deck, Amy would sashay her hips from side to side like a runway model. The debauched crew would stop and stare as she walked on by. For me, I was smitten with Amy from the minute I first set eyes on her. But unlike the depraved crew, I actually wanted a tried and true girlfriend, and foolishly thought Amy was that person. Unfortunately for me, Amy knew all too well what she wanted, and a serious relationship was not the case.

After getting my fill of the chauvinistic 2nd Engineer Bill, I walked away, and with that, Amy approached. She introduced herself, passed pleasantries, and then worked her craft on this young and rather wide-eyed boy.

CHAPTER EIGHT

"No group of individuals did more for establishing our country than the American Merchant Seaman and Privateers. Their record speaks eloquently of their devotion and sacrifices."

- John Adams

President of the United States of America

On my third day onboard the SHINNECOCK, we rendezvoused with the aircraft carrier USS JOHN C. STENNIS CVN 71, better known by her moniker *Big John,* for a major UNREP. Underway Replenishment, or UNREP in the vernacular of the specialty, is a critical necessity required to keep the combatant ships ready and in the fight. Moreover, it is also one of the most dangerous, if not *the* most dangerous operation, for ships at sea. UNREP is not for the faint of heart. You will routinely find up to a combined 165,000 tons of three large moving masses operating less than two hundred feet from each other, high-tension wires overhead carrying tons of cargo, the movement of petroleum at rates up to 15,000 gallons per minute through flexible rubber hoses, and crewmen working on deck and/or under the fuselage of specialized aircraft with their spinning rotors feet from their heads. Even more amazing is the fact that the massive amount of total tonnage, in the form of up to three vessels, is physically connected by wires. In the end, the ultimate goal of UNREP is the safe and efficient transfer of the maximum amount of liquid and/or solid cargo in the least amount of time, while not interfering with the combatant vessel's mission and enabling the Navy ship to remain on station indefinitely. When performed as designed, UNREP should be one of the many routine evolutions the combatant vessel accomplishes during its operational day at sea.

UNREP, as defined, is simply the transfer of liquid and/or solid cargo between two or more ships while underway. There are two general methods of such a transfer that may be employed. The first is the horizontal transfer of solid cargo and/or liquid cargo via high-tension wires and powered trolleys through specialized cargo and fuel rigs. This is referred to as *CONREP* or Connected Replenishment. CONREP of solid cargo is called Replenishment at Sea, or *RAS*. Examples of RAS solid cargo include food, stores, spare parts, mail, munitions, and even personnel. CONREP of liquid cargo is called Fueling at Sea, or *FAS*. Examples of FAS liquid cargo include vessel fuel, aircraft fuel, bulk petroleum products, potable water, and boiler feed water.

The second general method of UNREP is the transfer of solid cargo via specially designed or modified aircraft. This is referred to as Vertical Replenishment, or *VERTREP*. The aircraft are helicopters from the U.S. Navy stationed aboard the replenishment ship or, in this case, the SHINNECOCK. Examples of VERTREP of solid cargo include food, stores, spare parts, mail, munitions, and personnel. This may be achieved either through a cargo lift, which is connected under the fuselage through a specialized VERTREP pendant, or in some instances, transferred internally within the aircraft. It should be mentioned, there is no transfer of bulk liquid cargo via VERTREP, although the aircraft itself may be fueled while in the air hovering over the deck of the

UNREP ship in an evolution called Helicopter In-Flight Refueling, or *HIFR*, but this is not part of UNREP. VERTREP may be conducted either when the ships are conducting CONREP and are thus in very close proximity or when the ships are some distances apart. It is common to conduct CONREP and VERTREP simultaneously.

Briefly, CONREP is accomplished through the Standard Tensioned Alongside Method or *STREAM*. STREAM rigs were designed to permit greater separation between ships when conducting UNREP. The STREAM RAS rig employs the use of a tensioned one-inch wire rope highline, a hydraulic RAM tensioner at a maximum of 2,250 psi, and a trolley, which rides on the highline transferring the cargo. The trolley moves back and forth via both three-quarter inch in-haul and half-inch out-haul wires connected through a Standard Underway Replenishment Fixture, or *SURF* block. Peak loads should not exceed 10,000 lbs; however, the U.S. Navy is now developing heavy UNREP rigs, which would allow the routine transfer of greater safe working loads. The STREAM FAS rig employs one of two rig capacities depending on if sending a single refueling hose or a double refueling hose. These include a tensioned three-quarter inch or seven-eighths wire rope spanwire, a hydraulic RAM tensioner with 1,950 psi, a series of flow-through hose saddles connected to trolleys that ride on the spanwire, and a specialized fueling probe for the receiving ship. Of note is astern refueling. Although not conducted via a STREAM rig, nor alongside, astern refueling is UNREP and is utilized for those smaller vessels, which are unable to come alongside and withstand the pull of a high-tensioned FAS spanwire. Astern refueling is conducted through a smaller hose, at much lower pressure, and with both ships making bare steerageway through the water. Although not a common occurrence, it may certainly be considered a routine evolution for an UNREP ship.

Since ships similar to the SHINNECOCK may be assigned as integral part of the carrier strike group or carrier battle group, they too must be resupplied so they may support the strike group. Most often such ships will break off from the carrier strike group, which remains on station, and call upon a designated U.S. Navy or NATO logistic port, such as

Naval Station Rodman in the case of the SHINNECOCK. Here the SHINNECOCK will load solid and liquid cargo as well as personnel for the carrier strike group ships. Then following a brief resupply in port, usually an overnight, ships like the SHINNECOCK will race to meet the carrier strike group vessels on station, which is what we accomplished on my third day aboard, then the sequence will start all over.

However, there are times when the carrier strike group commanders prefer the UNREP ships such as the SHINNECOCK to remain with the strike group on-station at all times. In this situation, the SHINNECOCK would need to be resupplied at sea itself so as it can then continue supporting the carrier strike group in which it is attached. As such, another UNREP ship would act as a shuttle ship. That particular UNREP shuttle ship would go to the designated U.S. Navy or NATO logistic port, or in this case Naval Station Rodman, conduct the solid and liquid cargo lift, depart, and meet up with the SHINNECOCK, which has remained on-station with the carrier strike group. Then the two UNREP ships would conduct a type of CONREP/VERTREP called a Consolidation Replenishment, or *CONSOL*. It should be noted that these two vessels may be alongside each other for many hours, even over several days, if needed, conducting a simultaneous CONREP/VERTREP.

Operation of UNREP ships like the SHINNECOCK and the myriad of operations which take place during the UNREP evolution require exacting ship handling, complete knowledge of stability and trim, vessel hydrodynamics, and vessel interactions, such as bank cushion and bank suction effects, expert marlinespike seamanship on deck, superb solid and liquid cargo handling abilities, thorough coordination through exacting preparedness, and most importantly—the ability to adapt and adjust the plan in order to respond to any change or casualty to a particular piece of UNREP gear. On deck, the crew works like a well-choreographed ballet with cargo elevators bringing up cargo to the deck, fork trucks shuttling the cargo to the CONREP stations as well as to the flight deck where it is netted and prepped for VERTREP.

With the modern containerized merchant ships and Ro/Ro's there are few if any "stick ships," general cargo, and or break-bulk ships remaining. As such, it may be argued the fine art of deck seamanship is being lost. But not on an UNREP ship. In fact, there is such an abundance of marlinespike and overall seamanship involved, there are, as mentioned, two full boatswains, one for just UNREP, onboard SHINNECOCK—Bosuns Ramirez and Pickle, as well as a full-time ship's Carpenter.

Below the UNREP boatswain there are eight boatswain mates, or UNREP rig captains, tasked with leading their particular CONREP station. In a word, The UNREP ship is old school; whereas loading in port requires booms, most UNREP ships require use of the entire ship's cargo-associated equipage. When the cargo gets loaded in the holds, it requires copious amounts of dunnage, with blocking, bracing, tomming, shoring, and lashing the norm. When it comes time for the UNREP evolution, it is not uncommon for the UNREP Boatswain, Boatswain mates, and deck seamen to change a spanwire or a highline —while the other stations are connected to the ship alongside. There are occasions when the specialized wire rope slings that are utilized to ferry the cargo across may part. This was such a case when Bosun Ramirez performed a Flemish Eye and/or a Molly Hogan to get the cargo on the hook and transfer started again. While all of this seamanship is happening on deck, on the bridge the Master and ship's control, as the bridge and corresponding engine team are called, are also doing their part.

UNREP ships, akin to SHINNECOCK as the delivery ship, must determine the safest Replenishment Course, or *Romeo Corpen*, taking into consideration the customer or receiving ship, such as *Big John,* and follow on commitments, sea-state, traffic, etc. If, by chance, the SHINNECOCK would be the receiving ship, say during a CONSOL evolution, SHINNECOCK would have accounted for the hydrodynamic bank cushion and bank suction effect as the ship overtakes the other when coming alongside, an inherently dangerous operation. I was amazed that during my training at Ft. Schuyler I was repeatedly told to stay away from other ships. But this is not possible on SHIN-

NECOCK, as words such as rendezvous, join-up, come together, alongside, and bow-to-stern are normal terminology.

As I learned all of the intricacies of UNREP, I also desired to know the history behind UNREP. I understand the conception started after Spencer Miller of the Lidgerwood Manufacturing Company pioneered a device, which enabled a cable between two ships to remain taut. Then in November of 1899, off the coast of New York, the first attempt at UNREP was conducted between the collier USS MARCELLUS and the battleship USS MASSACHUSETTS BB-2. Instead of alongside, the two ships were moving in tandem bow-to-stern, and the speed of the cargo transfer was approximately 20-24 tons of coal per hour via the Spencer Miller taut cable system, a much lower transfer rate than was required.

On May 28, 1917, the USS MAUMEE AO-2 conducted the first modern UNREP. The executive officer onboard was none other than eventual Fleet Admiral Chester A. Nimitz. From this point forward, Nimitz played a key role in the development of UNREP capabilities and he utilized this extensively during WWII in the Pacific. Moving forward after WWII, UNREP continued to evolve, but remained a Navy evolution between two commissioned warships operated by active duty U.S. Navy personnel. As mentioned earlier, in the early 1970's the U.S. Navy realized both the new warships being delivered as well as the latest weapons systems were advancing technologically. Further, they needed their active duty sailors to undertake massive amounts of technical training and education to meet these new technology challenges. The Navy believed they could best be served by removing the sailors on the auxiliaries to possibly undergo the high-tech training, and then possibly follow on assignments to these new high-tech vessels. To accomplish such, the Navy shifted the operation of their marlinespike seamanship and the logistics heavy auxiliaries to include UNREP ships to operation by U.S. Merchant Mariners. To realize such, the Navy instituted a program called *Operation Charger Log II.* On May 4, 1972, the USS TALUGA AO-62 was decommissioned and then put into service as USNS TALUGA T-AO 62 operated by U.S. Merchant Mariners of MSC—and the program was an unqualified success.

Back to the *Big John* UNREP, it was exactly 06:00 and I heard the announcement over the ship's public address system, "Good Morning SHINNECOCK. The time now is 06:00; this is a callout for UNREP teams Alpha, Bravo, Charlie, Delta, Foxtrot, and Ship's Control portside. All stations to be manned and ready no later than 06:30, contact the bridge at that time with your status." Before I could sit up in bed, another announcement blared, "Flight Quarters, Flight Quarters, Now Set Flight quarters, Flight Deck Team man the Flight Deck, conduct F.O.D., walk down and report status to the bridge."

I have to admit I was a bundle of nerves, both excited and anxious, as my stomach churned. This would not only be my first UNREP, but it would be with the largest of ships, a nuclear-powered aircraft carrier. I quickly jumped up, got dressed, and rushed to my station on the bridge. I was on the Ship's Control Team, whereas my job was to stand next to the A/B helmsman as helm safety officer and watch that he strictly kept to the Romeo Corpen. I also manned the engine order telegraph and phones on the bridge if needed.

When I arrived on the bridge to take my station, it appeared to be controlled chaos with oodles of people milling around. Of course, there was Captain Jabba the Hutt on the port bridge wing stomping around like an elephant in heat using his vast vocabulary of four-letter words. "Romeo at the f***ing dip to port," he growled. Second Officer Matt took over the watch standing duties and navigation. First Officer Dashman stood next to Stone with coffee cup in hand, shaking his head probably thinking he can't believe he has to listen to this imbecile. It's a blessing in disguise that the crew is so skilled in UNREP that despite the intellectually challenged Captain Stone, we would perform flawlessly. Second Officer Matt would often mutter under his breath, "It's a good thing this ship is on automatic, despite the *Old Man*." Old Man is normally a seaman's term of endearment for the Captain.

Over in one corner on the bridge, engrossed in their communication duties, were the Navy operation specialists broadcasting to and fro with the carrier. There were also MSC supply personnel manning the phones with clipboards at the ready. Big Red, Amy and the other Navy signalmen were up on the signal bridge, handling all the signal flag hoists and sending flashing light and semaphore signals to *Big John* about 1,000 yards directly astern.

Down on deck, the UNREP teams busied themselves in preparation for the carrier to come alongside. We had four UNREP teams called out to man four UNREP rigs, three double hose FAS rigs and one cargo RAS rig. A double hose FAS rig consists of a large king post approximately 50 feet high from the UNREP deck, a three-quarter inch spanwire, a spanwire winch, two sets of approximately 300 feet of seven-inch fuel hoses, three flow-through saddles connected in between the 300 feet of hose, three saddle whips, a double fuel hose probe, and a 25-foot hydraulic ram tensioner. The double FAS probe is connected to the end of the fuel hoses, which are connected to the flow-through saddles, which in turn ride on trolley blocks along the high-tension spanwire, which is connected to the aircraft carrier. The ram tensioner keeps the spanwire taught when the two ships move in and out with the seas.

A RAS rig consists of a king post, a one-inch highline wire, a highline winch, an inhaul wire and inhaul winch, an outhaul wire and outhaul winch, a cargo trolley and a 25-foot hydraulic ram tensioner similar to the FAS rig. Once the highline is connected to the aircraft carrier, the ram tensioner will keep it taught and a cargo trolley with hook or hooks will ride along on the highline pulled over to the carrier by the outhaul wire/winch and brought back to SHINNECOCK by the inhaul wire/winch.

Each rig team included eight persons, led by a senior A/B called a Boatswain's mate, or *BM,* in the position of *rig team captain.* Don't get BM confused with Bosun. Recall the Bosun is the foreman while a BM works for the Bosun. In addition to the BM on the team, various non-officer crew would fill the other positions.

The next critical position is the winchman, who is tasked with operating the RAM tensioner, STREAM spanwire/highline, saddle whips, and/or inhaul/outhaul wires, which control the cargo trolley or fuel hoses.

The rig signalman utilizes two colored paddles to signal to the receiving station on the carrier. Next is a sound-powered phone talker, charged with relaying information to the carrier and then to the SHINNECOCK rig captain. The sound-powered phone functions on the principle of two tin cans with a piece of string taut between each, or on the vibration of one's voice. The sound-powered phone between the two ships cannot be intercepted or hacked like a radio signal.

Following the rig signalman are four line handlers. These folks pass the messenger lines to the carrier, which will eventually connect to the spanwire/highline to be connected to the carrier. These folks will also assist with hooking up the cargo on the RAS rig once the station is tensioned and up and running.

For this UNREP, we have teams Alpha, Bravo, and Charlie manning the FAS station numbers two, six, and eight. The RAS station is number four, which is manned by UNREP team Delta. Team Foxtrot are the folks who account for the fuel numbers; in other words, they are sounding or dipping the cargo fuel tank *ullages*, a method to calculate the amount of fuel in the tank, and relaying those numbers to the supply officer. He in turn then sends over a requisition, filled out in triplicate, to the carrier as they must *pay* for their fuels. Now paying is an anomaly, as no money, checks, or the like ever change hands, as its one Navy-owned ship charging another Navy-owned ship. Rather, it is all based on a line of accounting on massive spreadsheets kept deep in the bowels of the Pentagon somewhere, for the bean counters to scrub with every new administration.

The Ship's Control UNREP Team consists of all those on the bridge, as previously mentioned, plus those manning the engine room, after steering, and the telephone and distance or *T and D line* on the bow. In the engine room, along with old Chief Nowak, would be 1st Joof, 2nd Reinhart, one of the 3rd Engineers, an electronics technician, an electrician, and the refrigeration engineer.

The engine crew has to keep the engine and all the pumps, motors, and auxiliaries running during the UNREP.

In after steering sits the other Third Officer, Michael Shorter, another 3rd Engineer, and an A/B helmsman. This station is manned in the event the ship loses steering on the bridge. The Third Officer can take charge and have the A/B steer the ship so as not to collide with the carrier, a mere 150-200 feet away. The 3rd Engineer in the steering gear room is on call in the unlikely event there is a mechanical issue causing a steering casualty.

Stationed on the bow is the T and D team, led by the ship's carpenter along with two A/Bs. These folks send across a line, which provides distance markers so as the Captain can see how far apart the ships are steaming. In addition, there is a sound-powered phone connection to the carrier which is passed up to the bridge, so Captain Stone may speak directly with *Big John's* Captain on a secure phone.

Finally, the flight deck team, consisting of Ship's Bosun Pickle and eight more A/Bs, man the flight deck fire teams and cargo teams. At this point the two CH-46 helicopters stationed aboard SHINNECOCK from Helicopter Squadron HC-8, with the handle *Dragonwhales*, were already hovering in the air awaiting to start their *picks.* These are the loads that will be slung underneath the helicopter from the SHINNECOCK and then placed on the flight deck of the carrier. It is interesting how these picks function. First, the picks are made up of several stacks of cargo on 48-inch by 46-inch wing pallets. Each stack is netted in a large cargo net and bundles of three or four (up to six) cargo nets are connected together, depending on the maximum cargo lift weight of the helicopter. Then all the cargo nets are connected via legs to a five-foot pole pendant with a large eye. Next the helicopter will hover over the bundles of netted cargo pallets and a flight deck team member will run underneath the helicopter and take the pole pendant and place the eye to a large hook underneath the helicopter's fuselage. The deck team crewman then bolts for safety and the helicopter lifts the cargo off the SHINNECOCK and takes it to the carrier. When the two helicopters get in a pattern it's a thing of beauty to watch, almost like synchronized swimming. The first helicopter, or *helo,* makes a pick and then moves sideways to the carrier. In the meantime, the second helo is moving sideways above the first helo back across to SHINNECOCK after just dropping its load on the carrier and so on.

Once all the stations call in their status as manned and ready, Captain Stone gave his *eloquent* order to the signalman, "Two block Romeo to port, goddammit!" This meant the signalman on the signal bridge had to hoist the Romeo signal flag all the way to the top of the port yardarm. Once hoisted, the carrier, steaming directly astern of the SHINNECOCK at 1,000 yards, then knows they may proceed to come alongside the SHINNECOCK and commence UNREP.

Looking astern of the SHINNECOCK, I noted *Big John,* after seeing our Romeo flag hoisted, then hoisted her Romeo flag all the way to the top of her starboard yardarm, meaning she was commencing her approach.

This next maneuver is by far the most dangerous as well as the most awe-shattering of the entire UNREP event. The aircraft carrier JOHN C. STENNIS will start at 1,000 yards astern, increasing speed to about five knots greater than the SHINNECOCK's Romeo Corpen speed of thirteen knots. Next, *Big John* moves directly astern of the SHINNECOCK to about 600 yards. At this point the carrier alters course ever so slightly to the port to break the plane between the stern wake of the SHINNECOCK and the bow of the JOHN C. STENNIS in order to steam up and alongside SHINNECOCK. At 300 yards astern, the carrier's compass bearing is approximately six degrees from her portside to the SHINNECOCK's starboard side. At 175 yards astern of SHINNECOCK, JOHN C. STENNIS reduces speed to Romeo Corpen 13 knots. This is called the *coast-in* method of approach. There are many fluid dynamic effects in play at this critical juncture of the UNREP evolution and the risk of collision is at its zenith. Most notably are the bank cushion and bank suction hydrodynamic effects, as proved by Bernoulli in his aptly named *Bernoulli effect.* These two phenomena are most closely associated with shallow water effects on ships in narrow channels, hence their name *bank,* meaning the side of a channel. However, bank cushion and bank suction similarly affect two very large tonnage ships when interacting in such close proximity. As the carrier's bow passes the plane of SHINNECOCK's stern, her bow will veer slightly to the port, referred to as the *bank cushion effect.* This is due to the water pressure buildup on the area of the carrier's bow and the stern of SHINNECOCK.

Now the carrier moves bodily sideways toward the area of the SHINNECOCK's stern and quarter. This movement is caused by the increase in velocity of the water flowing through the restricted area between the two ships and the resultant reduction in pressure on the starboard side of the carrier and the port side of the SHINNECOCK.

Finally, when JOHN C. STENNIS' stern passes the SHINNECOCK's stern, the carrier's stern will shift toward the SHINNECOCK's stern, referred to as the *bank suction effect.* This is primarily due to reduced water flow in the area astern of the carrier coupled with the close proximity of the ship's propellers, or *screws.*

As soon as *Big John's* bow crossed SHINNECOCK's stern, a loud announcement was heard on the ship, "Bow to Stern Port Side." This was signaled from our stern lookout stationed on SHINNECOCK's fantail mooring station area. This announcement alerted the helmsman and the entire Ship's Control UNREP team that we were about to feel the bank cushion and suction effects and therefore should be prepared for immediate corrective maneuvers. Within seconds, I peered out the bridge wing blast hatch door and I could see the flight deck of the carrier moving by the bridge with the multitudes of fighter jets sitting on deck.

Once *Big John* was alongside SHINNECOCK, standing off about 150-225 feet, she matched our speed and remained *locked* in place. The carrier must constantly adjust its speed and course to remain in such, always remembering Signore Bernoulli and the fact the two ships will now tend to move closer to each other due to the increased water pressures between them. Second Mate Matt blasted the following announcement on the ship's public-address system. "Good Morning, Admiral Jones, Captain Smith, officers and men of the USS JOHN C. STENNIS, it's an honor to have you alongside the USNS SHIN-

NECOCK. We are standing by to receive your shot lines forward, midship, and aft on signal. Onboard SHINNECOCK, take cover." After this I heard in the background the carrier's PA announcement.

"Good Morning Captain Stone, Officers, and crew of the USNS SHINNECOCK. *Big John* is happy to be alongside. Standby to receive our shot lines forward, midship, and aft on signal. Please take cover." With that I heard the stations starting to sound whistle signals using their police whistles. Then BOOM, in unison, all the carrier's UNREP stations fired their M-14 rifles with line throwing attachments, sending parachute shot lines across the turbulent ripping seas separating the two ships and landing on the SHINNECOCK.

Next the UNREP stations teams on both ships go to work sending across their messengers that are attached to the spanwire and/or high-line, and sound-powered phone lines. On the flight deck they have already been making picks and drops while the carrier was coming alongside, the flight deck team continually fouling the flight deck with more and more cargo picks, as speed is of the essence.

After the rigs are across, the UNREP stations must put their wires in tension. That is yet another critical point, as the SHINNECOCK *rams down* on each station's hydraulic ram tensioner, the helmsman can actually feel the ships being pulled together! That's correct, the 100,000 ton JOHN C. STENNIS and the 50,000 ton SHIN-NECOCK are being pulled together by these powerful wires under unbelievable tons of tension. The UNREP teams on both sides are at great risk of injury and even death if one of these wires should part. But there is nothing that can be done; it is inherent to the job.

I am standing next to the helmsman taking notes from the UNREP, and I hear that all three double probes are seated, and we start pumping jet fuel. We are scheduled to provide the carrier with about one million gallons of JP-5 jet fuel. It bears reminding, *Big John* is nuclear-powered, thus no marine diesel is needed for the ship's engines, as such the only fuel needed is for the 80 or so fighter jets and associated aircraft aboard. With that, we get the word to start pumping jet fuel. SHINNECOCK employs its five massive cargo pumps, moving the fuel from her pressed-up cargo tanks out through six, seven-inch fuel hoses to the carrier at a rate of 15,000 gallons per minute. In a little over an hour we transfer over a million gallons to the JOHN C. STENNIS.

After about an hour into the evolution, Matt tells me I must go and relieve Michael, the other Third Mate in after steering so he can eat breakfast. Matt tells me to relieve Michael, send him to the saloon to eat, and then have him come back to relieve me, then I am to go eat and finally return to my station on the bridge. With that I turn over my duties as helm safety to Matt and depart for the after steering gear room.

Now, after steering, as you can imagine, is located in the bowels of the ship and all the way aft. This is the room where the steering engine room is located. Here one will find the rudderstock, or the actual top of the rudder attached to two horizontal hydraulic rams or pistons that physically move the rudder in the direction ordered by the bridge. There are also the motors and pumps, which power the hydraulic rams located in after steering. Finally, a *trick wheel*, as it is called, is also located therein, used to take control and steer the ship locally in the event of a loss of steering from the bridge. Therefore, there is a need to have a Deck Officer, an A/B, and an Engineer all stationed in after steering. Moreover, after steering is riddled with a very loud low-tone hum of the steering motors and pumps, which over the course of my career most definitely added to my hearing loss. On top of this were the high heat and humidity in the steering gear room. Ambient temps were in the mid 90's, with humidity to match. Additionally, neither fans nor blowers operated to move the hot disgusting air in a vain attempt to trick us into thinking we were being cooled off.

There were two 5-gallon plastic cans of boiler chemicals adjacent to the trick wheel and sound-powered phones. These were used as makeshift seats for the Third Mate and A/B, as actual chairs were not permitted. In fact, there was no sitting permitted so, of course, a mariner will make allocations, hence the 5-gallon can boiler chemical seat. In addition, there would be no reading or, heaven forbid, nodding off allowed. With that, I noticed a veritable library of old, stained, and ripped girly magazines, along with a few *Time* magazines.

After relieving Michael and sending him to breakfast, I sat on my makeshift boiler chemical container stool and looked around. The 3rd Engineer was lying supine on several spools of Manila line the Bosun had stored in after steering. I was thinking to myself, "Should I wake him?" There is a strict policy of no sleeping, after all, but this is the SHINNECOCK. The A/B sitting next to me was a watchstanding A/B with similar duties as my watch team personnel, like Leter, Waddams, and Stanz. However, this particular A/B was named Phil Corastas, or as the men called him, Phil *Co-rapp-us,* due to his pooping in his pants all the time. Phil had a disorder with the muscles in his rectum and he could not, for lack of better words, hold his bowels. If it was his time, the poop was coming out, head or toilet availability be damned. Corastas was in his 60's, but looked much older. He had a permanent scowl etched upon his face and was generally a negative fella. He did not have a good word to say about anyone or anything. To my surprise, as I sat near him in after steering, I saw he was a budding artist, or so I thought. Recall, no reading, no sitting, and no sleeping in after steering, but nothing was said about drawing. Corastas was sitting on his boiler chemical stool with a sketchpad in hand, working feverishly with pencils.

I couldn't help it; I'm inquisitive. I had to ask Corastas what he was drawing. Either due to wishful thinking on my part or naiveté, I thought he was sketching something in after steering, as he was sitting right there. Yelling at the top of my lungs over the din, I asked, "Hey, Corastas, whatcha got goin' on over there?" Unvarnished, he stood up and walked over to me.

"Take a look, Mate," he answered, as he showed me his sketchpad like a proud parent. I couldn't believe my eyes; in fact, I had to close and open them a few times to check myself. Old Corastas had drawn the most repulsive, abominable, and morally offensive pornographic and bestiality images; all from his most inner thoughts, mind you. As I looked, he actually started to explain the image and its meaning as if he were an art critic.

I pushed it away and said, "That's sick, in fact that's beyond sick, get it away from me."

Unfazed, Corastas shifted back to his boiler chemical seat, and commented, "I think it's very creative." He then continued on with his drawing. I couldn't believe what I just witnessed, and I wished I could erase what I had just viewed and gone back in time just five minutes so as not to ask Corastas anything, let alone about his sketches. I reminded myself, "I guess that's what I get for asking."

Finally, Michael returned to relieve me so I could go eat and get back up to the bridge to my station next to the helmsman. Relaxed in the fact I was departing the presence of A/B Poop-in-his-Pants, I ventured back above. When I returned to the bridge, I relieved Matt at the lee helm and took back my charge.

By the time I returned to the bridge from my time in unquestionable hell with *A/B Chester the Molester* Corastas, we had finished fueling the carrier, providing over one million gallons of jet fuel in just about an hour. FAS stations two, six, and eight were back onboard the SHINNECOCK and secured for sea. We were just wrapping up the cargo at station four. The cargo ranged from eggs to soda to spare parts to just about anything imaginable. For sheer comparison, every week we would send 55 pallets of soft drink cans across, totaling about 100,000 cans of soda. The carrier would expend that in one week! Just at that moment an announcement was blasted over the SHINNECOCK PA system, "Now Secure from Flight Quarters." The VERTREP evidently wrapped up as well when I was away from the bridge.

Subsequently, I heard station four call up to the bridge, "Last Lift Cargo Across, first lift of Retro," that being a nice term for the carrier's trash. Yes, garbage. Did I fail to mention we haul trash as well? Accordingly, pallets and pallets of nasty and funky smelling trash transferred back across to SHINNECOCK. Beside food refuse, there was plastics, general trash, hazardous waste trash, the hundreds of physical pallets that we sent over with all the cargo attached, nets, and even some medical biohazard waste for good measure. *Big John,* in essence, a small city with 6,000 residents onboard, generates a deluge of trash.

Finally, I heard station four call to the bridge, "Last lift of Retro, permission to break the rig." Without missing a beat, primitive Captain Stone started yapping out orders on his walkie-talkie radio to station four. "Station four, Captain here. Is there a package for me on that last lift?"

The rig captain dutifully answered, "Yes, Captain, there is a package for you as well as the box of cookies."

It is important to understand some of the traditions in regard to UNREP. Generally, the customer ship or the receiving ship sends its *thanks and appreciation* in the form of some baked goods to the delivery or replenishment ship. By the same token, the receiving or customer ship Captain also sends as a personal note and gift to the Captain of the delivery ship. Importantly, tradition also dictates that these items must be hand-delivered by the Cargo Officer himself from the UNREP station to the Captain on the bridge. Later in my career, when I was a Captain myself, I would always inform the Cargo Mate and rig captain to keep the baked goods for the UNREP station teams on deck and just bring up the personal package. I thought how selfish it was for most Captains to take the cookies themselves and not pass them on to the crew toiling away in the heat with the danger of death just a parted wire away. As expected, Captain Bulldog on SHINNECOCK, the whale-like subhuman he was, most certainly demanded the cookies all for himself. Crumbs at the corner of his oversized mouth with enough confections to satisfy a classroom full of kids, Captain Jabba the Hutt would then hand over the box to Matt to distribute to those in the bridge. I didn't partake in the pastries, as I usually felt for the men on deck. However, it's a good thing I never did such. As I later learned, some of the A/B's on deck would enact *similar gratitude* in which they thanked Stinky the Cargo Mate with his *seasoned* coffee cup.

Upon final distribution of the cookies and gift, I knew we were completing the UNREP and preparing for the carrier to break away. The station four UNREP team commenced *breaking the rig,* or essentially de-tensioning the highline wire and the retrieving the wire and all the hand-tended lines. The last line across was normally the T and

D line. When cast off, the command, "Last Line to Port" blared over the PA system. At that exact time, I could hear the carrier *pouring on the coal* or, in other words, I could hear *Big John's* engines revving up. Then the booming sound of the rock anthem, "You Shook Me All Night Long," by AC/DC reverberated across to the SHINNECOCK. In another UNREP tradition, the receiving ship, upon last line while commencing to break away, commonly will play a high tempo song on her PA system for both ships to enjoy as she steams off. The song played is aptly called the *Breakaway Song,* and right before the last line there is always anticipation on both ships' UNREP teams as to what will be the breakaway song, for only the bridge team on the receiving ship is aware.

As *Big John* kicked in the afterburners, the massive vessel, which I always felt was akin to a *Star Wars* battle cruiser in size and presence, shot past the SHINNECOCK. Of course, the helmsmen on both ships must again be keen with their handling, as the vessels continue to experience the bank suction and cushion effects. In less than one minute, JOHN C. STENNIS was past and clear of SHINNECOCK's bow and started peeling off to her port side with the UNREP mission completed.

CHAPTER NINE

"They're the Z-men. Z-men are the guys without whom General Ike's Army and Admiral Nimitz's Navy couldn't live. Five thousand seven hundred of them died from enemy torpedoes, mines, bombs, or bullets since our zero hour at Pearl Harbor. Z-men are the men of the Merchant Marine. They carry a big wad of identification papers in a book called a Z book, so they call them Z-men.

Listen, it takes nerve to go to work in a hot engine room, never knowing when a torpedo might smash the hull above you and send thousands of tons of sea water in to snuff out your life. It takes courage to sail into the waters of an enemy barbaric enough to tie your hands and feet and submerge you so you can drown, like a rat, without a fight. It takes courage to man an ammunition ship after you heard how Nazi bombers blew up 17 shiploads of ammunition at Bari and not a man was ever found. I was there about that time. I'll never forget it..."

- Bob Hope

Entertainer and Patriot

Christmas broadcast, 1944

My fourth day onboard SHINNECOCK started out seemingly normal; I was feeling pretty good about myself, as I was getting the hang of watch standing and learning about UNREP. I went up to the bridge to assume the noon to four PM watch and relieved Michael. He was in his typical good mood. To this day I always thought he was a hell of a nice guy with malice toward none.

After about an hour on watch, Captain Stone walked into the bridge. On this occasion he was somewhat presentable or, at least for the Bulldog, he was presentable. He wore a heavily stained khaki uniform shirt with the buttons barely hanging onto the buttonholes and, in between, rolls of fat bulged through. For trousers, he wore khaki shorts, of course heavily stained, with holes, with his rather generous belly hanging over and down in front. For feet coverings, Captain Stone slipped on a pair of overstressed Top Sider boat shoes with no socks of any kind. He then growled at me, "Get my chair set up on the port side wing."

I answered, "Yes, sir, right away." And with that I walked out to the port bridge wing, removed the chair cover, affixed a custom box for his walkie-talkie radio and binoculars and then walked back into the wheelhouse. "Your chair is ready, Captain."

The Bulldog mumbled something unintelligible and walked out to the bridge wing and proceeded to hop up on the chair. I thought, "I hope that chair can handle his weight." For a fat guy, Captain Stone had cat-like reflexes and could maneuver his mass with a certain degree of agility. At this time, I felt somewhat relieved; at least the Old Man was out on the bridge wing leaving me alone to navigate the ship. Unfortunately, my happiness was in passing, for as I looked out to the port wing, I thought I would vomit. Captain Stone had propped his feet on the bridge wing railing and unbuttoned his sullied shirt, exposing his distended abdomen. All I could think of was a beached whale dying on the sand. To boot, he started to snore like a freight train. Here it was, the early afternoon on a blistering hot and humid day in the tropics, and Captain Moron decided he wanted to sunbathe, to the detriment of everything decent. I resolved myself to just keep to my watch duties and leave the Captain alone. Maybe I will get lucky and Shellie will call him back to his stateroom for some afternoon delight. Ugh! The thought of that brought up a mouthful of lunch.

No sooner did I feel ill from the thought of Shellie and Captain Stone, that I heard on the radio, "Captain, come in. This is the Chief Mate." I turned and peered out the portside watertight blast door to see if the Captain was answering the radio call from the Chief Mate. However, it was to no avail, as the Bulldog wasn't budging from his recumbent position in his chair.

"Captain, come in; this is the Chief Mate," squawked the radio again. Once again, I looked out past the port bridge wing blast door and again Captain Stone was not moving from his blissful hibernation. I turned back to starboard and I saw LAS, the Cargo Mate, walking on the bridge. He told me he needed some information from the voyage plan for use with his cargo load program and he would stay out of my way.

"LAS, the Chief Mate keeps calling the Old Man on the radio and he doesn't answer. He's sleeping. Should I go out and wake up the bear?"

Stinky turned and, in a most stoic manner, replied, "Nah, never wake a sleeping bear. Just go out and make sure his radio volume is up and it's on the right channel."

Shaking my head in the affirmative, I concurred, "Great idea, I'll go do it right now."

I proceeded out to the port bridge wing and peered down at the Old Man's radio and, sure enough, he was on the wrong channel. I figured, I'll just change the channel to the correct frequency and be on my way. I reached down with my right hand and, as my fingers touched the knob, my arm was swiped violently to the side and, in doing so, exposed my entire chest. Before I could blink, Captain Stone's right fist hit me square between the nipples right on my sternum. As if at a funeral pace, I hit the deck, landing on my back, my head snapping to the rear and smashing into the steel deck. As I lay prone, I was having a hard time breathing, gasping for air.

Without even a hint of compassion, the poor excuse for a human being snapped, "You touch my crap again, I'll kill you. You understand?" I couldn't answer as I was still struggling to breathe after having the wind knocked out of me. Here I am at 150 pounds on the receiving end of a cold-cocked, full-fisted punch to the chest by a 450-pound behemoth. Captain Stone turned and vaulted right back into his chair as if nothing out of the normal had occurred.

Meanwhile, as I continued to lie on the deck, trying to gain my breadth and composure, I looked toward the door into the wheelhouse and there, staring right back at me, was LAS, standing silent. I thought to myself, "Ah, I have a witness to this physical abuse by none other than the ship's Captain. Eventually, I made it back to my feet and stumbled back into the wheelhouse of the bridge and walked across to the starboard side chart table as LAS was busying himself with retrieving the information he needed for the cargo load program.

Rubbing my chest from the blow inflicted upon me, I tapped Stinky on the shoulder, "LAS, did you see that? What should I do? He freaking knocked me out!"

As if repeating a mantra, LAS deferentially retorted, "I didn't see anything. I don't know what you're talking about." I was floored; I knew Stinky witnessed the entire assault and yet he would rather stay silent than be the honorable man and do the right thing. I turned and walked back to the centerline of the bridge; I had to keep it together for I was still on watch at the conn in charge of the safe navigation of the ship.

My watch ended without any further issues and I struck below to my stateroom. I walked down the three decks, taking heavy steps on each tread on the ladderwell. I opened my door, switched on the light, and plunked down at my desk, letting out a rather lengthy sigh. This situation is one that is incomprehensible to those who work ashore. I was totally alone with my thoughts, questions, doubts, feelings of abuse, and apprehension. Moreover, it was not as if I could pick up a phone and call home or even type out an email. I was utterly forlorn of any support systems. At that moment, I felt the oddest of feelings, one which I never experienced—absolute desolation. I can attest to the fact that I did not enjoy this gut-wrenching consciousness. However, I did know as much not to confide in anyone aboard, not even amorous Amy. Well, at the very least, the good news is we would be pulling into Rodman for our weekly port visit and resupply the next day.

The ringing phone awoke me from my restlessness; I picked up with the salutation of my rating in a groggy fog, "Third Officer here."

The voice on the other end was Matt, the Second Officer. "It's seven o'clock. This is your callout for anchor and maneuvering details for arrival, manned and ready by 07:30. Oh, and by the way early breakfast is also being served."

I perked up a bit upon hearing the word *arrival,* shooting back, "Right, OK, thanks."

As I hung up my phone, I thought about how the ship designers must have had input from a Captain or two as they mounted the phone on my desk, rather than by my bed. Obviously, this required me to actually get out of bed, place my feet squarely on the deck, and walk the two steps to pick up the phone. The placement of the phone was well thought, for had the phone been next to my bed, I very well may have hung up the phone and fallen back asleep. I proceeded to dress and get ready to head aft to the saloon for a quick bite to eat before taking my station on the bridge.

At approximately 07:20, I arrived on the bridge and took my station next to the helmsman. My arrival duty position is essentially the same position I assumed for UNREP, that of helm safety officer. The difference this time will be my additional duty of keeping the *bell book*, that being a specific logbook for recording the engine speeds, or *bells,* as well as key events, such as if a harbor pilot is aboard, when tugs are made up to assist the SHINNECOCK, and the like. On the SHIN-

NECOCK, being a steam turbine ship, the bridge employs the use of an *engine order telegraph,* or *EOT,* to indicate the desired speeds. The bridge will move a lever on the EOT, and a similar lever will move on an identical EOT in the engine room, and when the lever moves it *rings* a bell to alert the engineers of a new speed order.

Also, on the bridge for arrival anchor and maneuvering detail stood Captain Stone, First Officer Dashman and Second Officer Matt. Cargo Mate Stinky LAS was on the bow with Bosun Pickle and the anchor detail, making both anchors ready to let go in the event of an emergency. Down below in the pit of the engine room remained Chief Nowak, 1st Joof, and one of the 3rd Engineers. At the boiler flat were the 2nd Engineer Reinhart and a Fireman. The Fireman rating is not one whose job is to extinguish fires as one would think. Rather the Fireman on a steam ship operates the burners for the boilers to keep the fires burning in the boiler so as to keep making steam. He is a "fire-man" in the surest of sense.

At 07:30, we slowed to pick up the harbor pilot to bring SHINNECOCK into the port. The pilot was a part of the Panama Canal Zone Pilot Association, which at this time remained under U.S. ownership and control, and was considered U.S. sovereignty.

The pilot was an older gentleman probably at the end of his tenure. He was American, as was true of all the pilots in the Panama Canal Zone. In fact, he too was a long ago graduate of Ft. Schuyler not unlike Matt and me, of which Captain Stone was quick to alert the pilot. I actually held my head a bit higher, seeing the possibilities availed to my fellow alumni.

Of course, as soon as the pilot trekked his way up to the bridge under the escort, and conducted a brief turnover, old Bulldog hopped up onto his chair in the wheelhouse, leaned back and, to my astonishment, closed his eyes. It appeared the intellectually challenged Captain was perfectly fine turning over the ship to the pilot with zero oversight. A *harbor pilot* is a recognized, through qualification and certification, local area expert in regard to the complexities of the waterways and safe navigation. Further, he is contracted by the ship to assist the

Master in conning his ship through such regional estuaries up to the point of mooring with tugs. At that point, the harbor pilot will turn over to a *docking pilot.* Normally, an employee of the tug company the ship will use, and most likely a former tug skipper himself, the docking pilot is also contracted again by the ship, but this time due to his expertise in ship handling with tugs.

Pilots, both harbor and docking, are typically compulsory for all commercial vessels, but this is not necessarily the case for public vessels of the United States. However, it is always the prudent mariner, regardless of vessel, who employs a harbor and/or docking pilot. Most importantly, it must be reiterated, the Master does not turn over his authority of the ship to any pilot, which is the reason Captain Jabba the Hutt's specious act in dozing off was so troubling to me as a new Deck Officer.

"Time now is 09:00, deck department fore and aft," blared from the ship's PA system. I quickly indicated the time in the bell book, meaning the mooring details, which will eventually tie up the ship, are to report to their respective mooring stations on either the bow or fantail. I reached down, grabbed the sound-powered phone, and rang the annunciator. And with that I heard, "After Steering, Third Officer Shorter."

I provided the following instructions. "Hey Michael, go ahead to the aft mooring station and contact the bridge on radio. We are about to make up the tugs and start mooring."

Michael rightfully answered in the affirmative, "Roger, will do." And then I placed the phone back on the receiver.

The pilot was snapping orders to the helmsman, who happened to be A/B Stanz, who was extra alcohol "odor-ific." Stanz reeked of booze, so much so it must have awakened the sleeping bear, for Captain Stone jumped down from his perch and walked over to me. He leaned in to whisper in my ear, "Stanz stinks of booze. Why don't you shift him out with the A/B in after steering?"

Without missing a beat and almost aloof, I answered the Captain, "I thought of that too, myself, but you should see Waddams. He can barely stand."

Captain Stone looked down at me with his eyebrows perched up high, shaking his head in the affirmative, and in one of the most complimentary tones whispered, "Good call, Mr. Mate." Wow, I couldn't believe it, an actual adulation. I honestly didn't think he had it in him.

The docking pilot turned over with the harbor pilot. His job done, he went back into the chartroom where there is actual air conditioning. With that, the docking pilot, Captain Stone and Chief Mate Dashman both walked out to the starboard bridge wing. The next command I heard was for the bow and stern to make up their tugs. I quickly deployed the pen to the bell book and indicated the time. Captain Stone was barking out a myriad of engine orders, as I scrambled to ring up the EOT and mark the bell book. "Slow ahead starboard, stop port."

I answered, "Slow ahead starboard, stop port." A few seconds later, I shouted out, "Engine room answers slow ahead starboard and stop port."

This back and forth between the Captain on the bridge wing to me at the EOT continued for almost 30 more minutes and then I heard on the PA, "First line, shift colors." That's great; that means we are technically not underway anymore and *legally* moored. Notice I did not say *securely* moored, in order for that, the SHINNECOCK would have all 16 lines deployed and made fast. To shift colors, the signalman must haul down the *steaming ensign* flown from the main mast gaff and immediately raise the ensign on/off the stern as well as hoist up the Union Jack on the bow jack staff.

"Finished with the wheel," ordered Captain Stone. I confirmed the order and then directed A/B Stanz to head down to the gangway area to get ready to sign people on and off the ship and that I would be down shortly. With that, A/B Stanz departed as I continued to standby for engine orders—"All Stop" being the last order rung up on the EOT. I anticipated the next order would be the final and, with that, I heard over the squawk box amplifier for the sound-powered phone, "*Finished with Engines.*" Awesome, I thought, the first time I got to ring up "finished with engines," or *FWE.* My father used to talk about FWE with an air of reverence. It's one of the most important orders for the engineers. Of significance, only one individual may give the FWE order, that being the ship's Master. For once FWE is rung up on the EOT and answered by the engine room, it cannot be changed without a long and laborious process, as the engineers actually shut down all propulsion systems. It is certainly not a matter of turning a key as on a car. On a steam ship as is the SHINNECOCK, simply put, the fires are extinguished in the boilers. Without fires, there is no steam, and with no steam, there is no means to turn the turbines...hence no propulsion. With authority and purpose, I moved the EOT levers for both the port and starboard engines to "finished with engines." Almost immediately, the engineers answer the bell, finished with engines. There, I did it. My Dad would be proud.

Interestingly enough, my father had always told me that, when he died, he wanted a big propeller on his headstone and the words *finished with engines* etched in the stone. I always remembered his wish, and way too soon, I had to honor it. Just three short years later, I buried my best friend and father.

After ringing up FWE, I started to get ready to depart the bridge for the gangway and meet up with my perpetually inebriated watch team when Matt stopped me. "You want to go get a pizza tonight?"

Uncertain with his invitation, I replied, "Pizza? Where do you think we are—back home on Long Island?"

"They have a Pizza Hut on the base. It's the only restaurant, if you want to call it that."

Thinking, I said, "Pizza Hut—that's a sacrilege. But what the hell, OK. I got nothing better to do. Besides, I have the midnight watch tonight." After our brief conversation, I descended the three decks to the gangway.

I didn't have to think too long, for as I was heading down the ladder-well, who but Amy was on her way up. She stopped, in full-on flirt mode—eyelids, pouty lips, the works—and then looked at me and said, "Call me when you get back aboard tonight, I'm at extension 5-6-2." I tried not to seem too excited, but I was a young buck and I think I responded before she could get her extension out.

"Yeah, sounds great, see you later." She shot back her sultry look and we both went our separate ways.

CHAPTER TEN

"I trust Congress will soon provide similar opportunities to members of the Merchant Marine who have risked their lives time and time again during war for the welfare of their country."

- Franklin D. Roosevelt

President of the United States of America

upon signing the GI Bill, June 22, 1944

It's about one in the morning and I am on my in port watch on the bridge, correcting publications. We are moored at our usual pier at Naval Station Rodman in Panama for our weekly cargo load out, fuel lift, and resupply before departing to support the Navy ships at sea. Every week, the ships are sent out *Notice to Mariners,* or *NM,* which is a corrective action newsletter published jointly by the National Geospatial-Intelligence Agency (NGA), the National Ocean Service (NOS), and the U.S. Coast Guard (USCG). It is formatted to simplify the correction of all paper charts and nautical publications produced by NG, NOS, and USCG utilized for safe navigation. Law requires that all of such be corrected through the latest NM prior to transiting through a particular area. As the SHINNECOCK has a worldwide chart and publication portfolio, there is a substantial amount of corrections to perform. These may be implemented with a simple pen and ink change all the way to cutting and pasting the correction from the NM directly into the publication and/or onto the paper chart. The Second Officer, as the ship's official navigator, is responsible to the Master for all corrections; however, he routinely directs the Third Officers to handle all the publications as a collateral duty. The midnight to eight in the morning in port watch ordinarily is a quiet and low-key watch. This provides time for the Watch Officer to make corrections between his rounds of the ship. Unfortunately, this would not be the case for me this evening.

"Mate on watch, come in. This is the gangway," my radio crackles with Leter's slurred speech.

I unclip my radio from my belt, raise it to my mouth, and key the microphone, "Mate on watch, go ahead," I blurt into my radio.

"Hey Mate, we got a cab driver down here, he says he has one of the crew members in his cab passed out."

"Ok, I'll be right there." Then I proceed down to the gangway. Sure enough, there is a Panamanian cab driver standing right at the top of the gangway.

I approach him and he follows on describing the situation in his best-broken English. "Mira, man in taxi not moving," the driver stammers.

"OK, let's go take a look." So, the driver and I walk down the gangway, and then we walk all the way down the pier, past the gate with no lock, and old Waddams manning the pier access. As Waddams opens up the gate, I can't help but notice, he is doing a lousy job at trying to hide the can of beer in his hand. "Waddams, whatcha got in your hand there?" I ask.

"Oh, well, you know, Mate, it's hot out here, and the tiki bar is you know, right over there," as he points to the tiki bar. He is, in fact, correct; the tiki bar is a mere step away from the pier access gate which he was manning. Who the heck puts a bar at the end of a pier, certainly knowing the plethora of alcoholics onboard ships?

No sooner did I ask myself that question, that I had to hit myself. "It's genius. They will make a gold mine," I thought. Luckily, though, the now desolate tiki bar closed at 23:00. That being said, I thought again, "How did Waddams get the cold beer? Oh well, I don't have time to deal with this drunk, at least he's standing upright, now to the cab."

I poke my head in the back seat of the taxi and see it's A/B James O'Brien. After asking where the driver had picked up his fare and performed a cursory vital sign check, I ascertained he had indeed passed out from drinking. O'Brien is a big Irish-American in both stature and girth. I stood back up and thought, "How am I going to get this guy back on the ship? Heck, how am I going to get him out of the cab and down the pier?" Then the proverbial light bulb went off over my head. I knew what to do. On the pier were several dollies used to move the ten-inch hard cargo fuel hoses we had employed earlier in the day to load five million gallons of jet fuel.

"Gangway, Mate on watch, send Davis and Stanz down here to the taxi," I crowed on my radio.

With that I heard Leter's reply, "Roger, Mate. Sending the two down now."

While I was waiting for Davis and Stanz, I asked the driver what O'Brien owed him for the fare. The driver started to complain as to how much he had lost just dealing with O'Brien and pleaded his case for a larger fare. I didn't have time for this; I reached into my pocket and pulled out a $20 bill, held it out, and said, "Will this be OK?"

My favorite cabby snapped it out of my hand and walked around and sat in the driver's seat. No sooner had I been relieved of my twenty bucks, when I turned and saw Stanz and Davis stumbling down the pier, giggling, hooting, and hollering like a couple of hyenas.

"You two, cut that out and grab three fuel hose dollies and bring them here," I barked out my order. They rolled up the dollies and I said, "OK, let's pull him out of the cab, put one dolly under his upper torso and head, and the other two under his lower back and each thigh of his legs."

They answered almost in unison, "OK, Mate."

One, two, three...we extricated O'Brien from the cab and situated him on the three dollies; all the while he remained passed out. The taxi took off. Now all three of us, Stanz, Davis, and I crouched down and started rolling O'Brien down the pier toward the gangway. My rig was actually working; all that was dragging were O'Brien's feet that were hanging down from his upper leg and back of the dollies. Thank God the pier was rather smooth concrete vice gravel. We finally arrived at the foot of the gangway. I looked straight up and saw the accommodation ladder gangway almost vertical, as the state of the tide is at high water with the SHINNECOCK towering over the pier. I looked at Stanz and Davis and informed them there was no way we could get the jumbo and semi-comatose O'Brien up that gangway.

"Stanz, go to the linen locker and get me a couple of blankets and pillows," I ordered.

Stanz went scurrying up the gangway and Davis asked, "Mate, what are you going to do?" I informed my fine Crumb Boss that I have a plan, which may indeed workout.

Stanz returned, and I placed one blanket out on the concrete pier as if I were laying out a beach blanket. Next, I blurted out, "OK, you two, help me roll him over onto the blanket and let's keep him on his left side." The three of us methodically shifted O'Brien off the three dollies onto his left side. We then propped him in position with pillows and blankets. He wouldn't need the blankets for warmth as the temperature hovered around 93 degrees, even in the dead of night. I was more concerned with him aspirating any possible vomit and choking if he happened to awake and started regurgitating his liquid dinner. Also, I remembered from my ship's medical course, the left side is better as it puts less stress on the heart, and who knew if O'Brien had any heart disease along with his alcoholism?

With O'Brien securely in place, I followed Stanz and Davis up the gangway ladder and stopped at the podium where Leter was hunched over and drooling. I provided my guidance. "OK, all of you, move the podium over to the gunwale and keep a constant eye on O'Brien. Then walk down and check up on him every so often to make sure he's OK. Call me if needed."

If this occurred in today's atmosphere, this would have been a full-blown incident. In addition, to the Captain, First Officer, and Chief Engineer being awakened, O'Brien most likely would have been fired for cause with extreme prejudice. Add to this the reams and reams of paperwork filed and the subsequent safety work stand-down to conduct training on alcohol abuse, which would have all been mandated. Fortunately for O'Brien, these were the waning days of the Wild West and the romance of going to sea in the American Merchant Marine.

Matt and I were conducting our watch turnover on the bridge at about seven in the morning and I took him over to the starboard bridge wing and said, "Look down on the pier."

He belched out, "Who the heck is that?" I informed him of my evening's highlights with A/B O'Brien providing enough entertainment for ten watches. "Well, we've got to get him aboard before the Old Man sees him."

I stoically answered, "He's already seen him. The old man and Shellie came aboard about three in the morning. They were pretty liquored up, walked right by O'Brien, and up the gangway."

Now Matt was curious, "Did he say anything to you? Were you down at the gangway when the Old Man came aboard?"

"Oh yeah, I was there. I stood there like nothing happened and old Bulldog commented in passing if it was O'Brien down there. I told him it was indeed. And then the Captain was like, "Good job, good thinking. Then he and Shellie went to his cabin."

Matt, still floored, asked, "Did he say anything else? Did he blow a gasket?"

I looked at Matt, deadpan. "He said nothing else. And I wasn't going to push it. And that was it. So, are you gonna help me get him aboard or not?"

Matt stumbled in his reply, "Of course." Matt and I and now both of our watch teams, for a total of ten of us, met down on the pier next to O'Brien. However, this time, I brought a going aloft safety harness with me. We then proceeded to get O'Brien on his feet. He was still very groggy, but at least ambulatory. Yet there was no way he would make it up without massive assistance. We haphazardly had him don the safety harness and then connected a line to the D-ring on the front of the safety harness. We then helped O'Brien get upright and on his feet. He was shaky to say the least.

Next, Matt and I pulled on the line connected to the D-ring, whilst Stanz, Davis, and two other A/B's from Matt's watch pushed O'Brien from behind and we all went gingerly up the gangway. Once onboard, we removed the safety harness from around O'Brien, and Stanz escorted him to his stateroom. Another exciting in port watch came to an end.

After my fun with O'Brien on the midnight in port watch, I hit the *rack,* or went to sleep, in seagoing jargon. I awoke at about 15:00 so I could prepare for my next watch at 15:45. The four to mid in port watch is not as quiet as the mid to eight watch, but it is by far the most interesting, especially in regard to the crew. During this watch most of the crew will go ashore for their baubles and jubilation and then return in varying degrees of intoxication, all of whom will have a typical fish tale story. At this point, I must mention, no sooner did I take the watch from Matt, who had taken the watch from me eight hours earlier, that I proceeded down to the gangway to check up on my watch standers. When I arrived, Stanz stationed himself at the gangway podium, probably to aid in keeping him erect. Stanz reeked of alcohol, body odor, and cheap perfume which, by all accounts, originated at the old "good time Tami Nachi" or the local house of ill repute. I was informed Waddams was standing watch at the gate to the pier, conveniently located steps from the tiki bar, Davis was tending to his Crumb Boss duties, and none of them knew where Leter was located. So, all in all, situation normal for an in port watch on the SHINNECOCK.

At this point, I turn, and to my utter amazement, I sight A/B O'Brien walking down the deck with purpose, heading to the gangway. He looks at me and says, "Goin' ashore, Mate. Have a good one." With my mouth wide open, I couldn't utter a word as I was floored. Here was O'Brien, not eight hours removed from being comatose and catatonic on the pier to just about dancing a jig whilst stepping off the ship. "Now that's hardcore," I thought to myself. Most of us novices would need a day or two to recover; not O'Brien, he was rip roaring ready to go hit the bars again. In my head I was relieved that when he would return, I would at least be off duty.

The time was approximately 20:00 and Captain Stone walked up the gangway. I, of course, was present to meet him when he arrived at the top step. At least my watch team was coherent enough to inform me when they would see the Old Man walking down the pier. Jabba the Hutt approached me as he passed the gangway, and it appeared he was in an uncharacteristically good mood and thus seemed very approachable. He then kindly asked, "How is your first four to mid watch going?" Shocked in his rather normal demeanor, I related to him, "OK I guess, Captain, but I do have to ask, is it normal for the helicopter to move around while it's sitting in the hangar and we are tied to the pier?"

I could see the wheels turning in his head. The Captain, now inquisitive, replied, "What do mean, moving around?"

"Well, Captain, I was making my rounds not ten minutes ago, and I poked my head in the helo hangar and saw the helicopter moving up and down on its front wheel," I said, matter of factly.

Now I could see his jowls starting to turn and with that he shot back, "Show me."

"OK, Captain I'll take you to the hangar," I dutifully answered. The two of us then proceeded to make our way to the hangar. We entered through the forward hatch from the UNREP deck. No sooner did we enter the hangar than we both noticed the front of the helo, or bow of the fuselage, moving ever so slightly up and down on the front wheel shock absorber that operates like a piston.

It bears describing that the CH-46D Sea Knight helicopter is a medium lift tandem rotor transport helicopter introduced to the Navy in the late 1960's specifically for vertical replenishment and resupply. The CH-46D features a fixed tricycle landing gear system complete with twin wheels on all three legs of the landing gear that results in a nose-up stance, hence the colloquial name *Phrog,* as in a frog. The two-main landing gear protrudes from the rear sponsons, thus taking the bulk of weight of both the helicopter and cargo within. The third landing gear sits on a piston-operated shock absorber and is quite sensitive when the pilots are moving around in the cockpit, which is situated directly above such.

Now scratching our heads, the Captain and I are staring at the movement of the helo. The ship is tied up and not moving one iota whilst she rests alongside the pier. There are no air detachment personnel working on the helo, moreover, there is no one in the hangar at all. It's dead quiet. So why is this helicopter moving at all, even if slightly? Captain Stone had enough, and with me in tow, he stomped in his elephant-like fashion over to the door just aft of the cockpit, walked up the stairs into the cargo area. We both looked forward into the cockpit and to our utter amazement, there was Petty Officer Melissa Donahue, dressed in her birthday suit, atop of Lt. Kevin Williams while he is positioned in the pilot chair, in what I would describe as practicing for one's wedding night. Through the sounds of excitement from both romantic participants, Captain Bulldog roars, "What in God's green Earth is going on in here?"

With that, the amorous motion stops, Melissa looks up right at us and Williams turns his head, as he too is in the buff and almost in unison they utter, "Uh, Captain? Mate?"

Before either of the fornicators could utter a word, Captain Stone barked, "Cut this out, get dressed and meet me in my office ASAP… and be presentable." Then the Bulldog practically shoved me out the door to the point I almost tripped on the steps going down from the aircraft. When I stepped off the last stair, Captain Stone literally pushed me to the side and took off huffing, puffing, and muttering something incoherent. He then stopped, turns to me and said, "Get the air detachment O.I.C. and the military department Commander and bring them to my office."

I responded, "Yes Sir."

At this point I should probably describe the two willing participants in the erotic dalliance we just witnessed. Melissa Donahue was one of the female enlisted U.S. Navy radiomen, a part of the ship's military department. She was no more than twenty, maybe even nineteen; she had dark red hair, was well-proportioned, rather attractive, and in my very limited professional dealings, was also quite competent in her job. Interestingly enough though, previously she had asked permission to leave the SHINNECOCK a month prior to our return to homeport as she was due to get married. Yes, married, and not to Lt. Kevin Williams, either. He, on the other hand, was one of six pilots assigned to the air detachment assigned to the SHINNECOCK for the deployment. More importantly, as a Lieutenant, he was an officer, and fraternization with enlisted sailors is strictly forbidden in the Navy. Add to this violation of Navy protocol was the fact Lt. Williams was also married with children, which makes him an adulterer in the eyes of the Navy. Yes, as archaic as it sounds, the U.S. Navy also has strict rules and disciplinary actions against adultery.

I make my way to Commander Moore's stateroom. Moore is the officer in charge, or *OIC,* of the military department aboard the SHINNECOCK. He is an unassuming fellow with almost no personality. I would say he was an anomaly in that he was pretty much antisocial. I couldn't quite figure him out, though. He was rather effeminate, so I assumed he was gay, but being this was before the days where gays could serve openly, I dare not ask, nor would he ever admit to such a lifestyle. Moore was also 100% by the book and was not pleased with SHINNECOCK's loose reputation. I proceed to knock on his door. With that he opens and I pass on to him, "The Captain would like you to come to his office."

Moore, understandably bewildered asks, "What's going on? It's almost 21:00. Can't this wait until tomorrow?"

I take it upon myself to relay the fact as succinctly as possible, "He and I caught Donahue and Lt. Williams in the helicopter."

The Commander's eyes shot open, "What the ... ? Are you serious?"

I retorted, "Yes, as a heart attack. Now I have to go get Lucky," and off I went. Lucky is Lieutenant Commander Dennis Luciano, the OIC of the helicopter detachment; "Lucky" being his pilot call sign. It should be mentioned Lucky is the polar opposite of Moore. Albeit he is junior to Moore, Lucky has a wife and three kids, and is a graduate of Massachusetts Maritime Academy, one of the six State Maritime Academies, so he is essentially one of us—a mariner first—before he decided to commission in the Navy and fly helicopters. Lucky is very personably, kind, fun to go out on the beach with, and very professional. Just an all-around nice fella, and he did not seem to be bothered with the SHINNECOCK's free love, presumably as long as none of his people were roiled within such.

I didn't have to walk too far from Moore's stateroom to get to Lucky's, as his room was two doors down. Thankfully he was onboard, as he usually would have been ashore enjoying himself with one of the Mates, as he had a Third Officer license himself. After knocking on his door, he yelled for me to come in.

I entered Lucky's stateroom to find him sitting in the reclining chair in his sweats, feet up, watching a movie on his TV, complete with a bag of microwave popcorn. He looked up and said, "Hey Frankie. What's up, man?"

I felt terrible, but I passed on to him the details and I didn't mince words. "Lucky, the Old Man and I caught Williams and a military department girl in the helo."

Without missing a beat, Lucky shot back, "Williams, that idiot. Not only does he suck as a pilot; he is a sleaze. What a jackass." I shook my head in agreement, as I, too, had no use for Williams as a human being. He was such a classless piece of excrement.

One such an example had to do with Williams and his meals aboard. You see, Navy officers, unlike mariners, receive a daily stipend for their meals and then once a month they must stroke a check to the Chief Steward for any meals they consumed over that time period. Hence, the naval officers only pay for the meals they actually eat. On a U.S. Navy combatant ship, the officers do not have a choice in the matter, and they are charged for three meals-a-day at sea regardless if eaten or not. However, on the SHINNECOCK, Captain Stone was kind enough, imagine "Stone" and "kind" in the same sentence, I digress, to permit the pilots to pay only for the meals that they eat. Most of the six pilots and, specifically, Lucky paid for three meals-a-day regardless. Not Williams. He would skip dinner, and then in the most dubious manner, he would eat the night lunch, specifically prepared for the watch. He would take all the hoss-cock, cheese, and condiments and make a "Dagwood" sandwich. What Lt. Williams did not understand was that even the night lunch was not free, and if he partook in eating it, he needed to pay up. Finally, after the Chief Steward complained enough to the Bulldog, he acquiesced and made all the pilots pay for three meals a day, eaten or not.

After speaking with Lucky and Moore, I continue on to Captain Stone's office. When I reach his office, standing out in the passageway I find both Melissa Donahue and Lt. Williams, both dressed in their proper uniform of the day, mind you. I couldn't help myself, as I passed them, and crossed the threshold into the Captain's office, I muttered, "Nice to see you in clothes this time, Williams."

As I walked in, the Bulldog was at his desk, actually in some semblance of an official uniform and without lifting his head, he growed, "Did you get the Moore and Lucky?"

I properly answered, "Yes Sir, they should be up here momentarily."

Captain Stone looked up at me and instructed me to sit down on the settee and further informed me that I will remain here until dismissed. I thought to myself that this ought to be interesting. As I sat down, in walked Moore and Lucky, both dressed in their proper uniforms. Captain Bulldog then proceeded with his diatribe, "I am sure the Third Mate informed you as to why we are getting together and why two of your personnel are standing outside my office. I will be handling the shipboard consequences. As for the Navy *NJP* (non-judicial punishment), I will leave that up to you two." Moore and Lucky shook their heads in the affirmative. but said nothing.

Captain Stone continued, "Take a seat, gentlemen. I am going to call the first of the two participants in." With that, Jabba the Hutt shouted, "Petty Officer Donahue, front and center." Melissa walked into the Captain's office, pivoted smartly, and stood at attention, staring straight ahead in front of Captain Stone's desk. Now he spoke in the most authoritative tone I had heard from his disgusting mouth. "Petty Officer Donahue, we are all keenly aware of what transpired between you and Lt. Williams in the helicopter. As for your NJP, Commander Moore will be handling that aspect. For me, on the other hand, I am going to let you know my decision as to your request to depart the ship before we return so you may get married. My answer is you will not be permitted to depart early, and because you will miss your wedding, you are going to call your fiancé and tell him why." With that, Captain Stone pushed the telephone to the front of his desk so Donahue could dial.

With tears streaming down her face, but not a word spoken, she picked up the phone receiver and commenced dialing in front of all of us. I couldn't help but think how harsh a punishment the Bulldog was rendering, as it will almost guarantee the cancellation of a wedding and broken hearts for what may have been just some young indiscretion. Add to this sad fact the sheer humiliation this young woman will experience, having to pour out her heart and soul in our presence. But I am almost certain this was a part of the Bulldog's purpose as he had no conscience. Rather he was being purely a sadist.

"Hi, honey. I won't make it home for our wedding…" Melissa got out of her mouth between the sobs, and then, while we didn't know what her fiancé was saying on the other end, she broke down, wailing, with spurts of inhalation to catch her breath between the wails.

Chivalry was certainly dead inside Captain Stone's office, not one of the military officers present, and of course not Captain Stone, made any attempt to console this poor girl. I couldn't handle it anymore; I stood up, walked over, and put my arms around Melissa. Not in a romantic way whatsoever, but rather to console her, for I knew the next sentence out of her mouth would change her life forever. However, no sooner did I get my arms around her than I was forcefully pulled away by Moore and Lucky. The Bulldog belched at me, "Sit down and be quiet. Let her finish." I brushed off the two officers and sat back down on the settee.

As I was sitting down, Melissa spoke what would be her final words, "Honey, I love you, but I messed up big time. I didn't think and I, well, I…"

With that Moore jumped in, "Say it, tell him. We are all sitting here waiting."

Melissa, trying to compose herself, swallowed and finished, "I was caught with Lt. Williams…he's a pilot." Then silence, as I can only imagine what was being said on the other end. Melissa then uttered one word, "Yes." Which I could only imagine was the answer to the question did you sleep with him? Then she continued, "I am so sorry. I love you, OK. Please forgive me. OK…" That was it. She hung up the receiver and stood soldier straight at attention.

Captain Stone turned to Commander Moore and uttered, "Commander, this sailor is your charge for further disciplinary actions." Moore then spoke, "Petty Officer Donahue, this is inexcusable, and I am prepared to level my discipline at this time. I charge you with fraternization leading to fornication, and as such, you will be demoted one pay grade to seaman apprentice, and you will forfeit one week's pay. You are dismissed." Melissa vigorously turned and walked out of Stone's office.

At that point I went to get up and depart the office as well, but before I could even stand erect, Jabba the Hutt barked, "Where are you going? Sit down we have more...Lieutenant Williams, front and center." Kevin entered in a fashion very similar to Melissa, with purpose; he then pivoted and stood at attention.

Captain Stone spoke, "Lt. Williams, your participation in this hanky panky is even more egregious as you are both an officer and senior to the young Petty Officer. You clearly used your position and influence in destroying Petty Officer's pending marriage. Add to this selfish act on your part that you have a wife and children at home, seemingly waiting for their husband and father to return to them with honor. From my position, I have no control over your discipline, however, I did request you be sent back home to your squadron, as you are a detriment to our mission. Here is a phone for you to call your wife and let her know you will be coming home tomorrow."

Williams retorted, "Captain, Commander, and Lieutenant Commander, I take full responsibility for my actions and accept all the consequences. I am just sorry I had to bring you to this decision due to my lack of leadership." Then he picked up the phone and dialed. The difference this time was stark, in that Kevin showed no emotion; he was as cold as ice —no sobbing, not even a waiver in his voice when he spoke to his wife. "Sue...yeah it's me...Look, I will be coming home tomorrow..." Again, I had no idea what was being said on the other end, but I couldn't fathom the degree of indifference as he talked to his wife. "I was caught having sex with a Petty Officer." I couldn't believe my ears; he came right out and said it, not wavering one bit. Then he finished, "Yeah... I'll stay with them when I get home...Bye." My guess being he would not be sleeping in his own bed and, worse yet, I had the sinking feeling Williams had been down this road in prior instances with his wife.

Lucky then stood up and said, "Lt. Williams, I forwarded this to the squadron Commanding Officer, and he will be recommending courts martial. Go pack up your things, you are departing in the morning and, by the way, you disgust me. You are dismissed."

As I departed Captain Stone's office, I shook my head as I couldn't believe the degree of punishment and the perceived outrage by the Bulldog for two of the SHINNECOCK crew doing essentially what everyone else had been doing since I arrived, including the Bulldog himself. Later, I learned, it was due to Moore. Had Captain Stone not taken any action, Moore would have certainly gone off the ship to the Bulldog's senior managers at MSC and ask for his firing. My guess is Moore tolerated all the affairs within the ship as long as none involved military on military and/or could not be unequivocally substantiated. It must have been an unwritten, wink and nod agreement between the Bulldog and Moore. I made my way back to the bridge thinking, another day on the SHINNECOCK…

CHAPTER ELEVEN

"In some cases the men who man the merchant ships run even greater risks than the boys in the regular Army and Navy. When we realize that over and over again they land from one torpedoed ship and as soon as they recover from wounds or exposure they start on another trip; we can hardly fail to pay homage for their supreme courage."

- Eleanor Roosevelt

First Lady of the United States

June 1942

It was another quiet night on the midnight to four watch. Quiet is always good. There was not a hint of any shipping traffic in sight or on the radar scope. It was, however, hot as Hades and the humidity was almost one hundred percent, as we were sailing just north of the equator. It was this night I would be on the receiving end of some good-natured ribbing at the hands of the 3rd Engineer on watch.

Recall, the SHINNECOCK, being an old girl, had two 3rd Engineers on watch at all times, one at the control board in the engine room proper and another in the boiler room at the boiler's front to direct the Fireman. Engineers have very complicated names for shipboard equipment, which sound extremely impressive and intricate, requiring oodles of skill and knowledge to operate, or God forbid, repair. Of course, any complicated machinery, either actual or just by nature of the name, requires a great amount of overtime to repair… just ask an Engineer. Sometimes I think the Engineers love confusing the Deck Officers with the use of three-syllable gobbledygook machinery terms. Case in point, the Engineers thoroughly enjoy speaking of the intricacies of the *air handler* or for us mere mortals, the fan. Then there is the *purifier,* which sounds a bit more impressive than a filter. There is the *heat exchanger,* when discussing a radiator. The common dimmer switch for a light goes by the moniker *rheostat.* Fiberglass insulation is way too easy; better to use the convoluted nomenclature of *lagging.* These examples are a few of the Engineers attempts to confuse, befuddle, and confound the Deck Officers.

As my watch was progressing without incident, the dial telephone rings on the bridge. "Bridge, Third Mate," I belch out.

I then hear the voice on the other end of the line, "Hey, this is the 3rd in the engine room. We are having a problem with the number three air handler."

I perk up with this warning, "Is that serious?"

The old 3rd shoots back, "You better let the Captain know."

Now I am fully aware of the (perceived) seriousness and reply, "Ok, I'll let him know, call me when you get it fixed." With that, I hung up the phone and immediately dialed 7-1-1, the number for the Bulldog's stateroom. Even though I knew it was not a good idea to wake the sleeping bear, and he made that quite clear to me on my first watch, I had to notify him of an equipment problem or what I thought was such.

"WHAT DO YOU WANT?" Stone howled into the phone.

"Captain, my apologies, the 3rd just notified me that he is having an issue with number three air handler," I accurately reported. However, there was a distinct silence for what seemed like an inordinate amount of time, and then Stone blew his top, and I literally had to pull the phone receiver away from ear due to the din.

"YOU IDIOT! THAT'S A VENTILATION FAN AND HAS NOTHING TO DO WITH THE ENGINES"—after which I hear "click," as the Bulldog slammed the phone down, hanging up on me. I thought, sarcastically, well, that went well. I also knew the old 3rd in the engine room really got one over on me, in the worst way. So, I immediately dialed the engine room, and upon the phone being picked up, I did not even wait for the 3rd to announce himself. I jumped in, "Thanks a lot. The Old Man really gave it to me."

Laughing so hard, he had to gasp for breath to speak, the 3rd answered, "Welcome to the SHINNECOCK, Mr. Third Mate."

I smiled like a Cheshire cat and advised the 3rd, "You got me this time, enjoy it. Remember, what goes around, comes around. Bye."

After hanging up the phone on the receiver mounted to the bulkhead, I thought, how can I return the "favor" to the 3rd? Then it hit me! I would use the EOT's RPM annunciator dials. As mentioned, the *EOT,* or *Engine Order Telegraph,* functions to notify the engine room as to what speed the Watch Officer requires. At this time, on ship's similar to SHINNECOCK with steam turbines, all speed changes required an Engineer to physically open and/or close the steam throttle valves. The EOT comprised the following orders and/or commands, from the top to the right: ALL STOP, DEAD SLOW AHEAD, SLOW AHEAD, HALF AHEAD, and FULL AHEAD. From the top to the left, ALL STOP, FWE (Finished with Engines), DEAD SLOW ASTERN, SLOW ASTERN, HALF ASTERN and FULL ASTERN. Whenever a change is initiated on the EOT, a subsequent ringing of a bell sounds, both on the bridge EOT and on the engine room EOT. That ringing bell will only stop when the engineers match the command on the EOT in the engine room. In the vernacular of the mariner, the Watch Officer will "Ring Up A Bell Command" or simply, "Ring Up," and the Engineer in the engine room will then "Answer The Bell Command" or simply "Answer The Bell."

Each one of those commands corresponds to a specific shaft RPM speed. This would suffice for a commercial ship. Nonetheless, an UNREP ship, such as SHINNECOCK, needs the ability to relay to the engine room specific RPMs, which is needed when keeping station alongside another vessel in UNREP CONREP position. Therefore, SHINNECOCK's EOT had an additional three-dial annunciator attachment, which would also repeat on the EOT in the engine room. Adjacent to the annunciator dials on the EOT is affixed a push button bell activator. This activates the same EOT bell, which will ring automatically upon any speed command change until answered by Engineers. Obviously, this push button function is to alert the Engineer of a specific RPM change. I must emphasize, whenever the EOT bell "rings" in the engine room, the Engineer must be standing next to the steam throttle valves so as to add or remove steam to achieve the particular shaft RPM. The Engineer may not ignore any EOT bell in any shape or form. He must be laser-focused, awaiting the command.

With that in mind, I formulated my plan to gain the upper hand in the natural banter between Deck and Engine Officers. I walked over to the EOT, bent slightly down, and depressed the annunciator bell brass push button. I did not change the RPM's—rather I only wanted the bell to ring…at the EOT in the engine room. Sure enough, the bell rang in the engine room.

After ten minutes, the bridge dial telephone mounted on the bulkhead just aft of the telemotor helm started ringing. I picked up the receiver and calmly stated, "Bridge Third Mate." I heard heavy breathing with gasps of air on the other end; it's the 3rd in the engine room.

"Mate, is everything OK up there? I have been waiting for a new RPM order and nothing has happened."

I casually answered, "Oh, did I hit the bell accidentally? I am so sorry. Please disregard. You may stand down now from the throttle valves."

As I hung up, I chuckled a bit, to which A/B Leter slurred out, "Mate, why are you messin' with those engineers? You know they have their ways to get back at you."

I defended my actions. "Leter, after what he did to me tonight with the Captain, this is a walk in the park."

Leter came back, "OK Mate, I didn't see nothin'." The funny thing was I was not done cajoling with the 3rd that night. For I repeated the scenario two more times during the watch. Each time the 3rd was getting more and more angry and frustrated, but he knew he could not simply blow off the bell, as that may be the time, I really did ring up a new RPM order. Woe to the Engineer who fails to respond to an EOT bell. Undoubtedly, I never had any more trouble with the old 3rd for the rest of my hitch.

As is the case onboard the SHINNECOCK sailing in the tropics off the equator, foul weather, storms, and fog are common. A week or so after signing aboard the SHINNECOCK, I was on the bridge standing my regular noon to 16:00 watch. However, unlike most of my watches thus far, the weather was upon us, specifically rain. This meant one thing; I had to close all the portholes and the blast watertight doors on the bridge. Recollect the bridge of SHINNECOCK was void of any air conditioning or mechanical ventilation, save the portholes and blast watertight doors. With the rain, all of such were shut, closed, and dogged down to prevent water intrusion. Now the bridge was heating up—this was the tropics after all. Add to this the humidity of a hot house and you get the idea.

My uniform was literally stuck to me and I was sweating profusely, and the heat was emanating off my body. So bad was the sweat, I was ruining the navigation chart from the perspiration every time I affixed the ship's position. A/B Leter was on the helm and lit up a cigarette. The seamen's union required an ashtray attached to the helm to allow the A/B to chain-smoke, if so desired. I always hated cigarette smoke, and growing up in a house full of smokers that remained quite a challenge. Now with Leter smoking, I, of course, could not express my displeasure—again, union rules and all. As if on cue, A/B Waddams lights up as he is standing lookout on the port side of the bridge. Ugh! As if the heat and humidity were not enough misery, now I had two chain smokers in a room with no ventilation. Meanwhile the bridge is filling with smoke. I harken back to an old adage my mother would tell me when I was a boy eating dinner at a friend's house and I loathed what was being served. "Grin and bear it," she would say, so I figured I would try this in the smoking lounge of a bridge currently taking place. Unbelievably, not minutes after Waddams lights up, Stanz joins in the smoking party and he, too, lights up a Marlboro. The last straw occurred when Davis decided he too wanted a cig. Now all four of my watch team were smoking, and chain smoking at that, one after the other after the other. The bridge mimicked a fog bank due to the amount of cigarette smoke. I couldn't take it anymore. I turned around and addressed all four-watch standers. I calmly and politely enunciated, "Hey gang, I know you are permitted to smoke as per your Union, but would you please smoke one at a time?"

Of course Stanz bellowed for the group, "Mate, we are allowed to smoke, you know that."

I responded somewhat sheepishly, "I know. All I am asking is for one of you to smoke and when he finishes the next guy smokes. Can you do this as a favor for me?"

Stanz replied, "Mate, this is not normal, but I guess we could try it out this one time."

I responded quite sarcastically. "Thanks a lot."

"It's not normal," says Stanz. What a laugh! There was not one thing normal on the SHINNECOCK.

I finished the "smoke-eater watch," dropped below to my stateroom, and removed my uniform. "Whew!" I exclaimed out loud to absolutely no one. The clothing reeked so terribly it reminded me of the "smoking car" from the Long Island Railroad.

The next day, I am back on watch and it's a glorious day at sea. These days were those only one can imagine. Not a cloud in the sky, which for someone on land is not common, as low level fair weather clouds, called cumulus clouds, are an indication of land or an area at sea near land. You see cumulus clouds are those big billowing, fluffy, cotton-ball in appearance clouds well known during wonderfully beautiful days. At sea, these clouds are only visible in areas near shore. The SHINNECOCK was over 1,000 miles from the nearest land, and as such, there was simply nothing in the sky to obstruct the warm sun beaming down on the ship. More exciting was the crispness of the air, with zero haze present. This translated into the sharpest of horizon lines surrounding the entire ship.

The delineation from sky blue to the deep purplish hue of the sea was remarkable. Such a meteorological phenomenon is the mariner's best friend, as it enables precision sun lines and sights when using a sextant to navigate the vessel. Recollect, *GPS,* or Global Positioning System, had not been introduced, and transit satellite navigation, the very primitive precursor to GPS, did not lend itself to continuous precision navigation and establishing the vessel's positioning. Along these lines, not unlike mariners for centuries, tried and true celestial navigation prevailed. On a day such as this, with the knife-edge sharp horizon 360 degrees around the ship and the clear blue sky, it almost appears as if the ship is sailing in a continuous "dome." In such a way, many an Old Salt would often refer to a clear day at sea, as "sailing in the dome."

This glorious day at sea was interrupted by that pillar of seamanship, none other than Captain Bulldog—stomping up to the bridge, flinging the door from the chartroom to the bridge wide open and slamming it against the bulkhead and, in the process, out plodded the Old Man in all his huge disgusting and filthy glory. He was immaculately dressed, sarcasm intended, in a stained khaki uniform shirt, repugnant khaki knee-length shorts with no belt, no socks, and a pair of ratty boat shoes with the sides buffeted out due to his vile chapped, calloused, expanding bare feet. His fat belly was lopping over his shorts and the buttons on the shirt were barely able to stay connected.

Upon entering the bridge he barked out an order to me, "Get my port side bridge wing chair ready; it's time to get some sun." Oh boy, I thought, what is he talking about? I horridly readied his chair, taking the off the cover, attaching his seat caddy and inserting his walkie-talkie radio and binoculars. With that, Jabba the Hutt himself lumbered out to the bridge wing and, with an eerie creaking sound, slung his massive body into the chair. Finally, he pushed the reclining button on the chair and the back sank back. Next, in what I could not have imagined in my worst nightmare, he unbuttoned his shirt, out flowed the rolls of fat billowing over the sides, as if gutting a fish open. And with that, Captain Disastrous was content, resting fat, dumb, and happy...literally.

After witnessing such a display of utter revulsion, I needed to rush away so as not to puke in his jumbo eminence's presence. Extricating myself from this sight was wishful thinking, for at that moment, Captain Stone bellowed, "Third Mate, come over here. I want to tell you something."

Oh God, I thought, and what could he possibly want to pass on to me? It surely wasn't anything to do with the ship, course, or the like, because he was oblivious to day-to-day operations. No, I was rather correct, and dutifully answered, "Yes sir, how may I be of service?"

Captain Stone shot back, "I understand you have been complaining about your watch standers smoking?"

I tried to interrupt, "Well, Captain...."

He quickly shut me down, "Let me tell you something. Those men can smoke anytime or as much they want as long as it's not out on deck and during cargo loading. And listen closely: I can get a million Third Mates. I can't get a million good A/B's."

I timidly and almost inaudibly answered, "Yes, sir." I departed his enormousness and slumped back in the wheelhouse, reminding myself of a lesson one particular instructor provided back at Ft. Schuyler. You see, back at school they teach you everything you need to know to be an effective Watch Officer with one exception... effective and proper interaction with your unlicensed A/B's. That singular instructor's sage counsel resounded loudly in my head, "Do not get personal with your watch and do not get friendly with your watch." Astute advice indeed, but add to this the tip my mother had pressed upon me and my guidance was complete. She advised, "Familiarity breeds contempt."

The following Thursday we were making our weekly port call for cargo resupply at Naval Station Rodman in Panama. This port visit we were signing aboard a new Chief Mate, new Third Officer, and a new Chief Steward. I contemplated how sad it would be to see my first Chief Mate, Mr. Dashman, depart. As I mentioned, Dashman was retiring from the sea to teach fire and emergency techniques at the MSC fire school. I would always have fond memories of him. Third Officer Michael Shorter is a different story altogether. I always had a soft spot for him, as Captain Bulldog and Cargo Mate LAS constantly tortured Michael. I was happy for him; he would finally be heading back to see his wife and boys. As for the Chief Steward, Ricky Kaling, I had no real interaction with him, except at the midnight parties in 2nd Asst. Engineer Bill Reinhart's stateroom. I will miss Ricky's southern drawl and heartwarming, "Hey, Guy," which he used as a salutation. I will not miss his style of cooking and food choices.

After maneuvering alongside the pier with mooring lines deployed, Second Officer Matt Thule dispatched me from the bridge to the gangway area to get the in port watch ready.

After arriving at the gangway area, I stood back as Chips and the A/B's commenced deploying the ship's installed accommodation ladder ashore to use as a gangway. Without warning, I heard a screaming voice, "Hey, some guy just jumped off the ship!" I pivoted and saw one of the Navy helo detachment Petty Officers breathlessly repeating these words.

"What happened…who?" I proclaimed, looking right at the Petty Officer.

He looked at me, still struggling to regain his breath, and explained, "I dunno, one of the A/B's, I think. He just walked to the end of the flight deck, and stepped off, just like that."

I quickly asked, "Did he fall accidentally?"

The Petty Officer shot back, "No, it was intentional, he just walked off, like he meant to do it."

I thanked the young Navy sailor and informed him I would handle it from here. Not a second after reassuring the Petty Officer, a soaking wet A/B Chris Di Napoli sloshed past the frantic Petty Officer and me.

The sailor hysterically shouted, "That's him, that's the guy." Trying to quickly shoo the Petty Officer away and investigate, I thanked him and sent him on his way.

I turned back, looking at Di Napoli and quipped, "Di Napoli, what happened? Why are you wet?" A/B Di Napoli was one of the all-around best workers aboard. He stood medium height and weight, a nice looking fellow, well-groomed, certainly not in the style of the disheveled, alcoholic, and unkempt form of the typical A/B. In fact, Di Napoli did not drink at all as he was a teetotaler. He was well-read and versed, but extremely quiet, and always kept to himself. Further, he was neat—almost fastidious—in his appearance and the stateroom he shared. Di Napoli placed all of his items in individual sealable plastic containers and his rack, perfectly fitted, reminded me of room inspection back at Ft. Schuyler. Consequently, purposely walking off the ship was unlike him. A/B Di Napoli did answer my question, but not with a word—rather a shrug of his shoulders while standing at the gangway, water dripping down around him, forming a puddle. He muddled along, hopefully off to his stateroom to collect himself and change into dry clothing. In the meantime, I notified the Chief Mate of the entire strange incident. I thought…Strange? No, it's not strange for this is the SHINNECOCK after all.

As it happens, I experienced more oddities in regard to Chris Di Napoli in later years. Many years later, I served as Chief Mate on one of the newly built ships and we were docked in the port of Charleston, South Carolina. This specific ship sat alongside a pier in a reduced operational status, or *ROS,* along with a skeleton crew of which I was in charge. The time was about 21:00 and I got a distraught radio call from the A/B at the gangway, "Chief Mate, get to the crew lounge

ASAP. There is a fight." I leapt from my chair, sprinted out the door of my office on the zero five deck, and blurted into my radio,"Roger, on my way."

I flew down the ladderwell, seemingly levitating down each set of stairs, jumping out on the zero one level, swiveling my body one hundred and eighty degrees, and popped into the crew lounge. I stopped dead in my tracks, my eyes wide open, and I saw Di Napoli standing over A/B Kennedy, who was lying on the floor in a pool of blood apparently emanating from a wound on his forehead. All over the bulkheads I saw high velocity blood spray. Simply put, it looked like a murder scene. In Di Napoli's right hand, he clutched a *dogging wrench*; a red in color, twelve-inch pipe-like tool used to add leverage when securing watertight doors.

"Di Napoli, put down the dogging wrench and go to your stateroom," I ordered. Without expressing a word, A/B Di Napoli obediently complied and with a click, I heard his stateroom door closing.

I moved over to render aid to Kennedy, when he suddenly started to rise up, holding his head with his hand, blood gushing everywhere. I hastily grabbed him, snagged a towel at the sink, and helped him to a chair. I placed the towel on the wound and had him apply pressure. I seized my radio in my hand, and keyed in the microphone, "Gangway, this is the Chief Mate. Call 9-1-1 and get an ambulance here." From the corner of my eye, I saw two A/B's walking toward me, and I barked out, "Johnson, get a radio and stand outside Di Napoli's door and let me know if he comes out. O'Neil, help Kennedy down to the gangway and wait for the ambulance. We seem to have stopped the bleeding."

The two A/B's properly observed my orders and proceeded with their new duties. I urgently pressed on, climbing the ladderwell, and returned to my office. I promptly dialed the Naval Investigative Service, or *NIS*, again as noted, the precursor to the Naval Criminal Investigative Service, or *NCIS*. As this ship was a U.S. Navy government-owned vessel, only federal law enforcement agencies such as NIS or the FBI have jurisdiction and are permitted onboard. I explained the incident on the phone and that I had A/B Di Napoli secured in his stateroom. NIS dispatched agents and they were enroute to the vessel.

As the NIS agents arrived on the pier in two unmarked sedans with lights flashing, the ambulance carrying A/B Kennedy sped away at high speed with lights and sirens blaring. I met four agents, all dressed in suits with bulges protruding, hiding their weapons under their arms, at the gangway. We walked up to Di Napoli's stateroom and I dismissed Johnson from monitoring the door. The agents asked me to have Di Napoli exit his stateroom, as he would be more apt to follow my orders until properly in custody. I ordered Di Napoli, "Di Napoli, this is Chief Mate, open your door and come out." He submitted, opened his door, was handcuffed, and then hauled off to the local NIS holding cell. I ruminated to myself, what a night…now comes the paperwork.

The next morning, I received a phone call from NIS. Evidently, A/B Di Napoli hanged himself in his cell during the evening. I could not fathom the reality of this unobtrusive A/B alive one minute and dead the next. As per the requirements, I reported the crew suicide. The office sternly directed me by all means not to notify Di Napoli's next of kin, as that morbid duty resides with a special department, aptly called *decedent affairs*. Apparently, this department includes highly trained and specialized personnel to handle such situations with reverence and respect…or so I thought.

The next day, I received a phone call from Mrs. Di Napoli herself. I instantly thought that she, now having been notified properly by the department of decedent affairs, would request the return of her husband's personal effects. Again, here I am assuming the MSC office to be competent, but this is MSC after all. In actuality Mrs. Di Napoli asked me, "Is everything alright? I haven't heard from Chris in two days and he always calls me every night at nine PM sharp."

I was floored. My ears must have been deceiving me. Was it possible the decedent affairs office was so delinquent it had not contacted this poor woman? I moved quickly in responding to her, "Mrs. Di Napoli, did MSC contact you?"

She responded with some trepidation, "No, why would they? Is there something you're not telling me? I just want to talk to my husband."

With all the compassion I could muster, I replied, "Mrs. Di Napoli, you really need to contact MSC, that's all I can say right now." Needless to say, she hung up the phone without another word. Furious, I dialed MSC's decedent affairs department. Answering the phone on the other end was the typical dull government employee, not unlike customer service at the local department of motor vehicles. After a few minutes of the runaround, I finally reached a decision maker within the department. Unbelievably, the person or persons assigned to contacting Mrs. Di Napoli had misplaced his file… in one day mind you... and just moved on. Heartless, I thought. These are the same people at the office, who if their child falls down and scrapes his knee, act as if it's a life and death medical emergency, even taking several days off to cope with such a harrowing experience. Conversely, if a mariner's child suffers an accidental amputation of a digit and he requests time off before signing on to a ship assignment, the same MSC desk denizen summarily dismisses him with the phrase, "You're a mariner, aren't you? So, you must go." Your child be damned.

The question remained, what had caused such a commotion for Di Napoli to almost kill Kennedy? As it turned out, Kennedy admitted he instigated the entire brouhaha. Ostensibly, Di Napoli was minding his own business and watching the television. Kennedy explained he did not care for the show and decided he was going to change the channel. Without even asking, Kennedy picked up the remote and changed the channel. Di Napoli immediately shot around and demanded the channel be returned, as he was in the lounge first. Kennedy then made the fateful mistake of demanding Di Napoli "make him change the channel." Well, Di Napoli being, well, Di Napoli, rose up from the settee, strode out into the passageway, removed a dogging wrench from its holder adjacent to the watertight door, returned to the lounge, and without saying a word proceeded to beat Kennedy about the head. It must have been by divine intervention, which allowed that specific dogging wrench's construction to be aluminum rather than the normal steel pipe. For had that dogging wrench been composed of steel, A/B Kennedy would surely be dead.

Back on the SHINNECOCK, after Di Napoli trudged to his stateroom in a state of soaking wetness, I contacted the Chief Mate, and he subsequently sent Di Napoli to the Navy hospital ashore for a psychiatric evaluation. Di Napoli was preliminarily diagnosed with a mental disorder and repatriated back to the U.S. Foolishly, I thought that would be the last I would see of A/B Di Napoli, but as it turned out, his condition was never reported properly, and he continued being assigned to ships until that fateful night. Yet again, my adage holds true. Recall "going to sea, you are either an alcoholic or insane." In this case, poor Di Napoli was undeniably batty.

CHAPTER TWELVE

"A true sea power must have a vibrant merchant marine..."

- Alfred T. Mahan

The Influence of Sea Power Upon History: 1660-1783

Published 1890

Our new crew members started boarding the SHINNECOCK and signing aboard. First Officer Martin Borg presented himself at the gangway and produced his identification card permitting A/B Waddams to transcribe his name and rating in the official gangway log,

Borg, Martin, S.S.N. 237-90-9234, First Officer,
reports aboard for duty

Incidentally, this log entry is different from those crew members departing the ship, as was the case when Third Officer Shorter signed off at the gangway with A/B Waddams logging,

Shorter, Michael, S.S.N. 465-78-8994, Third Officer,
Departs the vessel, bag and baggage.

Ever since my first day writing the official logbook and adding in the phrase *bag and baggage*, I thought quite odd. *Bag and Baggage?* Why not simply log "departs the vessel with bags," or why log anything at all to do with a crew member's luggage? I later discovered the term had a legal connotation that meant "all of one's belongings," especially with reference to departing the vessel completely and totally, nothing remaining.

All of the crew knew of Chief Mate Borg, as his reputation in the fleet preceded him, and not in a positive manner. Borg was originally from the country of Malta, more precisely the city of Gozo. Chief Mate Borg had the unflattering moniker as the *Bozo from Gozo*. At thirty-five and a hawsepiper, Borg had worked his way up to Chief Mate, but developed many enemies along the way. He was rather on the shorter side, maybe five foot eight inches, but in good shape, with jet-black wavy hair, and a bit of an accent when he spoke. The other distinguishing feature was his inability to enunciate clearly. In fact, understanding Borg was so difficult, he was said to speak as if he had marbles in his mouth. Add to the fact that he screamed when he did speak with his trademark garlic buffalo breath. The crew was understandably upset, as they were losing the kind and charming Mr. Dashman, and gaining the petulant Mr. Borg.

Even Captain Stone sulked knowing MSC assigned Borg to SHINNECOCK. Apparently, in an attempt to ingratiate himself to MSC with a possible promotion to Master, Borg flung a prior Captain under the proverbial bus. All the MSC Captains were well aware of Chief Mate Borg's allegiance or lack thereof; as such, he could not be trusted. What an unnameable position in which to place a Master of a vessel. The Master needs his full faith and confidence in his number two, and the ability to trust that number two with his doubts and insecurities concerning ship and mission. If unable to expect such, the Master must constantly look over his shoulder and by all means never descend the ladderwell in front of such an untrustworthy Chief Mate.

As the story goes, Borg was Chief Mate on a NEOSHO class of UNREP oilers and the ship was getting ready to depart from, ironically, Naval Station Rodman, Panama. The same Rodman in which SHINNECOCK now rests. Borg was on the bridge; the harbor pilot was aboard, the tugs made fast, with all crew at their stations. Missing from the bridge, however, was the Captain of the ship, and the ship may not sail sans the Master on the bridge. In this case, the Captain was in his stateroom, with a massive hangover from the previous night on the beach. Chief Mate Borg was well aware of this fact, and moreover, the fact that the Captain was an alcoholic, following precisely to my tried and true hypothesis: a mariner must either be an alcoholic or insane. The pilot and tugs were getting impatient, and departure time had passed by some fifteen minutes. The Second Officer sprinted down to the Captain's office and attempted to rouse him out of his rack and drunken stupor. The Second Officer also relayed the fact that Chief Mate Borg was itching to get the ship underway without the Captain. Back on the bridge, Borg refused to wait any longer for the Captain and informed the pilot to get the ship underway. The pilot balked, "Without the Captain on the bridge?"

Borg proclaimed, "I am the Captain now!" As if on cue, the Captain walked on the bridge and dismissed Borg from his duties, striking him below.

Chief Mate Borg would soon aim his ire in my direction.

Also signing aboard was the new Third Mate, Rob Harrington, a hawsepiper who prior served a hitch in the Navy as an enlisted quartermaster, and had only recently been promoted from A/B to Third Officer. At twenty-eight, Harrington stood six-foot-three, tall and stocky, a little on the heavy side weighing 260 pounds—simply, think football tight end proportions. He was quite the character, very personable, with an infectious laugh, and disarming demeanor. We fostered a good friendship, with him actually inviting me to stay in his home when the ship moored in Norfolk. That in itself appeared very generous, as I at the time continued to reside on Long Island. His generosity allowed me to get away from the ship and relax. At this point, I should add, Harrington was a lazy man and would always try to find the expedited method, even if not then in accordance with the regulations.

One time when we were back in our homeport of Norfolk, I was turning over the in port watch to Rob. Since we were in homeport, he naturally would go to his home at the oceanfront of Virginia Beach where he lived. On this day Rob was relieving me at 23:45 for the midnight to eight in port watch. I would be *dogging* the watch, and as such, I would be relieving Rob at eight in the morning. At about 23:30 Rob walked up the gangway and asked that I meet him in his stateroom for turnover. I knock on his door and I enter his stateroom; it appeared he was changing into his uniform…or so I thought. As I opened my *wheel book*, mariner-speak for a memo pad, and started rattling off all of the notes to turn over to Rob, I looked up and he was folding down his bedding. He then slowly eased under the covers just as I was finished briefing him. Without missing a beat Rob announced, "Hey Frankie, sounds great. Just leave the radio and keys on my nightstand…and on your way out, please shut off the lights… Thanks." And with that, I complied and departed, thinking…sleeping on duty? Not accidentally nodding off, rather purposely hitting the rack, was unbelievable.

Unfortunately, Rob also suffered from another mariner malaise, the siren's calling. Although not a true lady's man in the mold of 2nd Assistant Engineer Reinhart, Harrington loved the ladies, and appearance was an afterthought. About six months later when the SHINNECOCK was moored in her homeport of Norfolk Naval Station, the time was 07:30 and I was relieving him for the eight-hour in port day watch. However, instead of his usual civilian attire to go ashore, he was all decked out, with slacks, jacket, tie, and full of *fu-fu juice,* or overbearing cologne. I had to ask, "Rob, what's with your get-up and all the fu-fu juice?"

He smiled and released one of his bellowing laughs, then looked at me and in all seriousness informed me, "The carrier departs for deployment at eight o'clock. I need to get to the Chief's club to pick up a six-month wife."

I must have looked somewhat befuddled, but gave a quick, "Uh huh." I dared not ask, as to give off the impression I was a novice, but I later discovered the meaning behind Harrington's cryptic comment. I would learn when a Navy aircraft carrier deploys for six months, with a crew of 5,000 men at the time onboard, thousands of wives remained behind, many of whom preferred to have a special someone to keep them warm on all those long and lonely nights. Not long after waving goodbye to their husbands, just long enough until the carrier sailed out of sight of land, these same wives would race off the pier, arriving at the Navy Chief's club to meet their prospective six-month husband. They would then hook-up with a man with all involved knowing the expiration date for their rendezvous, namely one week prior to the carrier returning home. The Navy sailors on the carrier may have had an inkling of their wives pending transgressions. The sailors would often refer to the infamous "Jody" who is taking care of their wife while they were deployed. I guess Harrington was "Jody" and it bothered him not, as he had no conscience when it dealt with women.

Also signing aboard this port visit at Rodman was the new Chief Steward, Kane Stanton. Kane was quite the character; he was from the South, African-American, in his late fifties, medium height and build, with his head closely shaved. However, it was his matter of dress that was remarkable. Kane would wear suits the color of highlighter pens, with a fedora hat to match…in the same color, with a feather affixed. On the day Kane signed aboard, he wore a school bus yellow three-piece suit and hat to match. He looked like the pimp character, *Huggy Bear,* out of the 70's TV cop show *Starsky and Hutch.* The crew called him the "Kane Man." All this aside, Kane had a reputation of being an outstanding Chief Steward both in quality of meals as well as keeping within a budget, although he had a strange way of getting his ideas across. A few weeks into his hitch on SHINNECOCK, Kane and his team of steward utility men discovered what was referred to on ship as the "Mad Pooper." In other words, Kane discovered remnants of a crewmember who decided to use an alternate location to defecate than the head. Yes, it can be rather disgusting, right up there with the 3rd Engineer turd chaser hanging his finds in the elevator. Evidently, in one department head meeting, Kane made a point to bring the situation of the Mad Pooper to the attention of the group. When the Captain suggested Kane pay the steward utility men hazard pay for cleaning up the feces, Kane went further. He went into great detail as to how he could ascertain the pile of crap was not actually deposited at the spot originally, rather it was produced somewhere else and then carried and placed in the particular spot in which it was discovered. Yuck! Needless to say, the entire group of department heads, as well as the Captain, had enough of Kane and his Mad Pooper crime scene investigation.

Well it didn't take long for Third Officer Rob Harrington to fit nicely into the debauchery that was SHINNECOCK. Two days after we got underway from Rodman for our weekly fleet resupply, I was heading to the bridge for my midnight to four AM at sea watch. As is proper and professional when relieving a deck watch at sea, the officer must follow some tried and true and, later in the century, required regulations. The professional mariner would arrive for his night watch about twenty-to-twenty-five minutes before the hour. Recall we try to relieve by quarter to the hour as a courtesy, although technically, the oncoming Watch Officer has until the hour. The Watch Officer would first get a cup of coffee and stroll out to the bridge proper. He needed to let his eyes and senses adjust to sheer darkness at sea, especially with no moon about. The oncoming Watch Officer may then walk out onto the starboard bridge wing, as the starboard side is the burdened side in vessel crossing interactions and take in any traffic or ships within visual sight. Next, the oncoming Watch Officer would walk back into the bridge and examine the radar for contacts and possible close quarters situations.

Reading and signing the *Master's night orders* follows. These are specific orders or directions from the Captain with which the Watch Officer must comply during the overnight whilst the crew and primarily the

Captain are in their beds, otherwise referred to as *racks* or *bunks*. The night orders always end with the order to contact the Master at any time or if in doubt, and to do so early, so as to give the Master enough time to evaluate any potential situations prior to *extremis*. This is described at the point at which action by the burdened or *give-away* vessel alone will not prevent a collision; thus mandating the vessel with right of way or the *stand-on* vessel take avoiding action. Obviously a situation a Watch Officer should not wait to develop before contacting the Captain. As such, this is an area where young or inexperienced officers often fall short, that is, such officers fail to call the Master early as directed. This may be due to the fact that many officers incorrectly feel that by calling the Master they have failed in their duties, when in fact, by contacting the Master early, such officers will actually have the reverse effect and actually gain the Master's trust and respect.

If the Master can trust the Watch Officer will call him early and when in doubt, the Master may then actually be able rest in the evening, knowing he will be called no matter what with plenty of time to rectify any pertinent situations or, God forbid, a potential catastrophe. It should be noted, in port, the Master's Night Orders are written by the First Officer, as they primarily deal with cargo operations, ongoing or planned, personnel issues, signing aboard or departing, as well as port-specific items. But with the at sea night orders, the final line is always to call the Master if needed, early and/or in doubt, with the added caveat that he may contact the First Officer first when in port. However, a Watch Officer can never go wrong in notifying the Captain…ever. Maybe I should add the qualifier: competent and professional Captain.

This was not the case with Captain Bulldog Stone, for on one of my first night watches, I actually called him, as directed. As mentioned, Captain Uncouth himself did indeed have that key sentence in his Night Orders, that is, to contact him if needed and/or in doubt. However, he obviously added the line to cover himself in the event of a casualty. You see, that night I had to maneuver for my first contact, and having some doubt, I called him. I actually had to wake the bear and I could tell he was not pleased. Within seconds, the door flew open from the chartroom and, as usual for Bulldog, he flung the door open so wide, it slammed against the back bulkhead. However, this time, I thought the door would be torn off the hinges. Next, Captain Stone stomped like an elephant out to the bridge wing where I was standing. Of course, he was in his normal uniform of the day, disgustingly filthy khaki shorts and yellowed, ripped t-shirt with rolls of fat billowing out and around. However, this time, he neglected to wear any foot coverings. Yup, he was stomping out with his cracked and calloused feet splayed out on the deck.

As he approached, I had not had a chance to utter a word before he bellowed, "What the hell, Third Mate…If I need to be up here, why do I need you? Well…? Do I need to be here or not?"

The point was made quite clear that night, so I gulped and said, "No Sir, my sincere apologies." And with that, I learned never to call this imbecile ever again…in any situation. Insult me once, shame on you, insult me twice, shame on me, I thought. Unfortunately, there came a time in my hitch where I really needed his assistance on the bridge—and not due to my fault—but still I did not call the fool.

In continuing discussing the Master's Night Orders, I need to note that such must be distinguished from the *Master's Standing Orders*. As the Night Orders are specific to that one day and/or night, the Standing Orders are the Master's general instructions for all Deck Officers onboard the ship accounting for most potential shipboard operations, emergencies, situations, and contingencies. The Master's Standing Orders are always in full force and must be read, understood, and signed by every Deck Officer upon signing aboard for duty. It cannot be emphasized enough the Night Orders do not supersede the Standing Orders, rather they supplement them.

After the oncoming Watch Officer reads and signs the Master's Night Orders, he will read any Watch Officer turnover notes and/or any message traffic or official U.S. Naval messages, weather reports, distress reports, etc. Next, he will examine the ship's course, both gyro steering compass and the magnetic, and he will note the status of the engines. The relieving Watch Officer may even ask the helmsman the question,

"How's she steering tonight?" The response from the helmsman may be, "She's taking a few degrees of left rudder to keep on track" or "I can't hold her within five degrees, and she needs me to give large rudder to hold her."

At this point the relieving Watch Officer goes to the chart table and inspects the night's run, and most importantly puts down a position. The Watch Officer must know, at all times, the ship's position. The worst words a Captain can imagine upon asking a Watch Officer, "What's the ship's position?" would be such an answer as, something to the effect of, "Let me check and get back with you."

In addition to affixing the ship's position, the Watch Officer will note any set and drift the vessel is experiencing, how far ahead or behind the ship is in regard to the intended voyage plan, any upcoming planned course changes, if changing charts, etc.

Finally, it is at this point, when the relieving Watch Officer approaches the off going Watch Officer (and it bears mentioning during the entire time and up to this point) that the off going Watch Officer does not disturb the oncoming or relieving Watch Officer, who then announces, "OK, I feel pretty good about everything. What do you have?" The Watch Officer being relieved will then essentially go over everything the oncoming Watch Officer examined prior on his own. Specifically, the off going Watch Officer will announce the gyro steering course, the magnetic steering course, the engine status, RPM, percent pitch, and/or speed, and end with any contacts and or traffic. The last words always end with, "Any questions?" Secord Officer Matt took that a bit further with his dry sense of humor, ending with, "Any questions, comments, or general unhappiness?"

Never allow a mariner an open-ended question such as "Any general unhappiness," for the mariner would go on and on.

This is the critical point, for when the oncoming Watch Officer is ready to assume the watch, he would repeat the gyro steering course, magnetic steering course, the engine status, and end with, "OK, I got it." That's how it is done in the U.S. Merchant Marine. Rather informal as compared with U.S. Navy, but remember the U.S.

Merchant Marine are professional mariners whereas the U.S. Navy are the warfighters. Needless to say, in the Navy, there would be almost a ceremony during the change of a routine watch, which may even include waking the Navy ship's Commanding Officer as well.

Back on the SHINNECOCK, when I was relieving Third Officer Rob, it was about twenty minutes to midnight and I was in the aft chart-room administering myself a first cup of caffeine infusion, when the door opened from the sweltering hot bridge and Rob popped his head through. Now at this point, I had not even commenced my pre-turnover duties and routine as delineated above. Rob then barked, "160 degrees on the gyro, 150 degrees on the magnetic, 75 RPM on both engines. Gottta run, Jeanie is waiting for me. See you..." My mouth was probably wide open with my coffee stirrer ready to fall out. For at this point I'm in such utter disbelief, I couldn't even muster the word "WAIT" out of my mouth. If I blinked, I wouldn't have noticed, it happened so fast. Evidently, Rob urgently needed to meet Jeanie. Jeanie Mahoney was another radioman enlisted military department girl. She was a little on the older side, all things considered, say thirty, not attractive at all, and was married with several children. Marriage and kids aside, Jeanie liked men and was very open about her dalliances. She once proudly related a story to me as to how the previous Second Mate, prior to Matt, a Greek fellow named Stavros Killios, would "have" her right on the chart table while the ship was underway. And I'm not referring to the chart table in the aft chart room. No way. I mean the chart table right on the bridge in front of the A/B helmsman. Well it was at night and it was dark on the bridge, but still, quite the exhibitionist. I can only assume Jeanie put her sights on Rob in a matter of days since his arrival.

In any case, after having the watch dumped on me, whilst what seemed like minutes but was probably mere seconds for me to collect myself, I darted out the door onto the bridge. What a predicament Rob had just let fall in my lap, and my eyes had not had enough time to acclimate to the dark. I ran to the radar, I checked for traffic, hmmm, no traffic, but land off both sides of the vessel. I next dashed to the chart table and checked Rob's last position. Not trusting this position, with land around us and plenty of physical aids to navigation, or *ATONS*, I took a round of bearings. Immediately, I plotted my lines of position…Whoa! Low and behold, Rob's position was way off, we were heading for the coast and were coming up on a traffic lane between two small islands. Oh my God, I thought, we could run right aground. Headlines go running through my head, "U.S. TANKER RUNS AGROUND ON COAST CAUSING HUGE OIL SPILL," or "NEW OFFICER RUNS SHIP AGROUND—OIL SPILLS ON THE BEACHES." Without a minute to spare, I altered the ship's course to split the two islands, then I ran from the bridge wing gyro repeater to the other side bridge wing repeater shooting bearings, plotting, and adjusting course as necessary. In one of the series of me running back and forth, between bridge wings, I slipped on the ultra-high polished teak bridge wing decking, my feet flying forward from underneath me, and "bam," I landed flat on my ass.

The noise of my falling must have awakened A/B Leter from his usual stupor, as he yelled out, "You OK out there, Mate?"

Propping myself back up onto my feet, I sheepishly reply back, "Yeah, I'm fine, just my pride." I had to think to myself, why would anyone put super slippery teak decking with no anti-slip or anti-skid coating on a bridge wing of a ship? But, no time for all this contemplation as to ship construction, I had to make certain the ship was going to split the two small islands and not run aground. It bears repeating, there was no GPS, no Loran-C outside the U.S. and, as mentioned, the Transit SatNav system was very suspect at times. As such, this required my ability to put exact positions down on the chart in rapid succession, all the while keeping keen situational awareness.

After about an hour, I successfully navigated the ship safely through the two small islands, away from the coast, and returned to the traffic lane. By 03:00 the area in question was approximately sixty miles astern when I dialed Second Mate Matt for his routine watch wake up call. Rob arrived on the bridge at 03:40 and conducted his pre-watch routine in preparation for taking the conn, and then approached me for the final turn over of the watch. But before I could rattle off the requirements for him, he asked, "How was the watch last night?"

I answered nonchalantly, "No issues, just routine."

With that, Rob contemplated out loud, "That's the way we love it… watch boredom equals no casualties."

Little did Rob know of the sheer terror I faced not three hours prior. In my short time as a Third Officer, I had the undesirable honor of experiencing the one percent of sheer terror, of the meme, a watch being 99 percent boredom followed by one percent sheer terror. Upon my successful relief by Rob, I descended the ladderwell and entered my stateroom and just collapsed in utter mental exhaustion.

Years later, when I had the time to think about this exciting watch, I knew I was wrong. In the study of marine casualties and near misses, we speak of the *error chain.* Marine casualties, such as fires, floods, collisions, groundings, sinkings, or near misses of such casualties, are normally not the result of one catastrophic event. Rather they are the result of a series of smaller, somewhat innocuous incidents which eventually lead to the catastrophic marine casualty or even the near miss. Each one of these smaller incidents is referred to as *links* in the *error chain.* The key to success in preventing the marine casualty or near miss is removing the *first link* from the error chain. After such, the entire series of events that follow would not occur, thus preventing the catastrophic marine casualty.

In my case on that memorable watch, the link in the error chain is identified as the moment Rob poked his head through the bridge door and belched out the turnover information before bolting to meet up with his courtesan. It was at this point in which I should have acted in the following manner: I should have stopped Rob right there and refused to take the watch until I received a proper turn over. Had such occurred, I would have certainly discovered Rob's inaccurate plots and follow-on impending doom to which the ship was heading. Or, if Rob refused to provide a proper turnover, I should have then immediately contacted the Captain to come to the bridge. This again would have removed the first link in the error chain. In actuality I did contemplate calling Captain Stone to the bridge during my running back and forth plotting positions, but recalled the Bulldog's words to me, when I did call him to the bridge at the beginning of my hitch. He was crystal clear in his disdain for actually…um…adhering to his own orders, that being to call him anytime when in doubt. Therefore, I did not call. I was lucky; the outcome most certainly could have been catastrophic. This was just another example of how not to be a Master, courtesy of the incompetent Captain Stone.

CHAPTER THIRTEEN

"To the spread of our trade in peace and the defense of our flag in war, a great and prosperous merchant marine is indispensable. We should have ships of our own and seamen of our own to convey our goods to neutral markets, and in case of need, to reinforce our battle line…"

- Theodore Roosevelt,

President of the United States

Last Annual Message to Congress

December 8, 1908

Chief Mate Borg did not disappoint when it came to living up to his antisocial and cruel reputation. We had arrived back in Rodman after another week at sea for our usual refuel and resupply prior to servicing the fleet again. After dinner I decided to go ashore to the Tiki bar at the end of the pier for a cold highball cocktail. As I was preparing to walk down the gangway, I ran into the paint locker man, A/B Julio Hernandez. The ship's paint locker being A/B Hernandez's work center, where he would mix and issue paints, thinners, epoxies, brushes, rollers, and the like for use by both the deck and engine crew. Onboard a complex and large crewed vessel such as the SHINNECOCK, the paint locker man was a most important position. For besides the mixing of paints, his duties included inventory control and procurement of paint and paint accoutrements. The downside of the job may be the constant exposure to all the fumes and volatile organic compounds, and this was before the wide use of respirators. Needless to say, A/B Hernandez probably killed a few good brain cells tending to his duties. The other oddity A/B Hernandez dealt with was his status as a recovering alcoholic. Recall my adage, in order to go to sea you must be either an alcoholic or crazy. However, what I failed to mention is the wrath of the recovering alcoholic mariner. This individual may be even more annoying than the drunk. You see, most of the recovering alcoholic mariners, and there are quite few, are all "Friends of Bill W" —William Wilson, the founder of Alcoholics Anonymous and its infamous 12-step program and the look for a higher power.

On those occasions when I would venture to the fantail to listen to the ship's scuttlebutt, I would often run into the A/B Hernandez smoking as the paint locker itself is situated in the fantail vicinity. After exchanging pleasantries, Hernandez would, invariably, start proselytizing about his higher power and the evils of drinking...any drinking. While I am all for religion, of any kind, especially out here with all the debauchery and wickedness, I don't need Hernandez's brand of worship shoved down my throat. As far as I'm concerned, a mariner's beliefs are his business. What Hernandez and the recovering alcoholic mariners of the same ilk lack is the understanding that drinking does not necessarily make one an alcoholic. These mariners believe that any drinking, even for those not afflicted with alcoholism, is inherently evil and must be stopped...at all costs. And as such, these folks go to great lengths to convince any unsuspecting mariner of that fact, obtrusiveness be damned. When A/B Hernandez would begin his advocacy stump speech, I would politely depart the fantail. *Well, there goes some peace and relaxation*, I would think to myself.

Back to the SHINNECOCK and my going ashore for that drink at Rodman while running into A/B Hernandez.

As I prepared to step foot on the gangway to proceed down to the pier, Hernandez yelled out at me, "Hey, Mate, where ya goin'?" Not knowing who just called out to me, I turned to the right and looked to see A/B Hernandez.

Realizing I may be here for awhile because amongst other things, Hernandez is long in the tooth, I shot back, "Going to get a drink."

Like a freight train, Hernandez shot back, "Don't do it, Mate. Don't go. It's not worth it. It's of the Devil. Look to your higher power." I thought, I knew it, I just knew it, on cue, and Hernandez delved right into his righteous diatribe.

However, this time, I was not so polite. I couldn't bite my tongue any longer and as such, I shot back, "Hernandez, just because you can't handle a drink doesn't mean I can't have one from time to time. Believe me, I am not going to let it get out of control. I am allowed to do this."

Stunned, Hernandez didn't say anything, for about a nanosecond. As I turned and stepped smartly down the gangway ladder I could hear Hernandez in the background, "I got you, Mate. I will be here when you get back, and I'll save a seat at the Bill W. meeting." Good old Hernandez just didn't fathom the reality of the fact I could drink and still be OK. Interestingly enough, maybe twenty years later, I ran into Hernandez at a Spanish restaurant in Norfolk. As it turned out, he retired from the sea, married, and opened up a restaurant. He was still the same Hernandez, preaching to anyone who would listen, but his food, unfortunately, was not that tasty and yes, as expected, he served no alcohol in his restaurant. I do give him credit for turning his life around.

I walked with a deliberate step and purpose down to the end of the pier and the Tiki bar, knowing in that tropical heat of over 100 degrees a cold margarita awaited. When I arrived, I sidled up to the bar next to Third Mate Rob, who was accompanying his ship paramour Jeanie for drinks. After some small talk, I started to look around and, to my utter dismay, there was Chief Mate Borg trying his best to gain the attention of Vicki Burns, another military department enlisted female radioman. Although, this time, it was clearly not mutual. My chivalrous and gentlemanly senses started to perk. My mother's words rung clear: "never be a cad and never allow a woman to be victimized by a cad." What's more, I knew Vicki was recently married and had one son from a previous marriage. In addition, according to the other military department girls aboard, Vicki was ever true to her husband and never strayed. This held true even with the axiom to which they so often referred, "What goes on deployment…stays on deployment." However, it looked as though Borg was putting on a full court press with Vicki in his sights. It was overly apparent, even to me as just arriving at the Tiki bar, that Borg was plying Vicki with drinks…lots of drinks. Everyone knew Vicki was lonely and upset for having to leave her new husband and young son. Chief Mate Borg only signed aboard one week earlier, but could sense this like a wolf to carrion. This boor took full advantage of Vicki's weakness and was in the process of exploiting it.

As this was continuing, I looked around the bar, and no one was the wiser. Borg was making a play, and no one was going to step in and help this young woman. With that in mind, I nudged Rob sitting next to me, for he was in deep conversation with Jeanie. Rob knew that after the drinks, the two of them would return to his stateroom. Rob turned to me, overly annoyed that I disturbed him, and commented, "What? What is it? Can't you see I am busy here?"

I shot back in a low tone, "Rob, take a look at the Chief Mate. Doesn't he look like he is making a play for Vicki, getting her liquored up?"

This mattered not to Rob for he answered, "Maybe. So what? She's a big girl and he's a big boy, and hell, this is the SHINNECOCK… everyone have fun tonight."

He then turned and continued his exhilarating conversation with Jeanie about the romances aboard the SHINNECOCK. Well, I couldn't just sit there, but as I was thinking about this, I looked over and saw Vicki and she was wasted drunk, she couldn't even keep her balance. Next I saw Borg put his arm around her and attempt to start walking back to the ship with Vicki on his arm. At this point, it appeared she was so inebriated, she was like a lost puppy, just following the man home. All of a sudden, the bartender yelled out to Borg, "Hey man, you didn't pay for all those drinks." Borg turned, dropped his arm from Vicki's waist and returned to the bar, presumably to settle up on the bill.

It was now or never for me if indeed I wanted to help Vicki get rid of this scoundrel. I hopped off my bar stool, dashed to Vicki, and quickly escorted her through a small partitioned area off the back of the Tiki bar, out of sight of Borg.

After seeing we were safely hidden from view, I stopped, turned toward Vicki and said sternly,"Vicki, what are you doing? Borg is trying to get you in bed. He got you drunk."

Just like that she glanced at me with bedroom eyes, wrapped her arms around my neck, pulled me, and breathlessly bemoaned, "I love you and I always wanted you." Then she pressed her lips against mine and kissed me.

I quickly pushed her back and retorted, "Vicki, you are lonely. This is not right. I am getting you back to the ship." I immediately grabbed her hand and hurriedly ran back to the ship, almost dragging poor Vicki in tow, as she was barely able to stand upright. When we reached the gangway, I maneuvered behind Vicki and helped push her up the gangway ladder as she held the railings.

Once at the top of the gangway, we boarded the ship, and Second Mate Matt was standing right there along with Cargo Mate LAS. The comments, as expected came calling, "Whoa, what have we got here?" bellowed Matt.

Followed by LAS, "What's Amy going to think when she hears about this?"

I turned my head, shot a look back to the both of them, which could have turned them into stone, clutched Vicki by the shoulders as I walked her toward the watertight door into the forward house, and barked, "It's not what you think, Borg was on the prowl…talk later." We then navigated our way through the labyrinth that is the passageways of the SHINNECOCK's interior layout, all the way to Vicki's berthing area. Recall, the military department enlisted lived in mass berthing in bunks three high. As we approached her bunk, and thank God it's the bottom bunk, I jockeyed Vicki to lay down in her bunk; she tried to pull me in bed with her.

I quickly released her clutch and reminded her, "Vicki, you need to just sleep it off." And with that, I departed the berthing compartment. Thankfully, the place was empty, as a male is forbidden from entering the space. But again, all bets are off on the SHINNECOCK.

After putting Vicki to sleep, I ventured out on deck and was planning on dropping in the saloon for a snack, when I ran into Chief Mate Borg. It's about 22:00 hours, but the ship is lit up like Yankee Stadium at night due to all our deck lighting. Borg beckons me over with a hand gesture, which to any of the Filipino crew would have been akin to calling me a dog. I couldn't attempt to ignore him, as we clearly made eye contact. I walked toward him, knowing I was going to get a mouthful of words, garlic breath, and marble speech.

He mumbled, "I am going to get you for what you did tonight."

Sarcastically, I made like I couldn't understand his marble mouth, and replied, "I'm sorry, Mate. What did you say?"

With that, he repeated, "I said, I am going to get you for what you did tonight."

Again, trying to mock him, I repeated, "Mate, I am really sorry, I can't understand you."

At this point, I could see he was turning red and getting ready to have a Maltese eruption, so he barked, "Dammit, you know what I am saying...watch your back."

He and I both turned and walked away, me heading to the saloon, Borg heading to try again with another military department girl. You see, Chief Mate Borg was not only cruel and harsh with the men, he was a creep and somewhat of a lech. It was well known on SHINNECOCK that Borg would peer into officer stateroom portholes and the like to see who was sleeping with whom. What a real jerk.

It did not take long for Chief Mate Borg to administer his retribution for my running interference in his attempted assault of a female the previous night. The next morning, I had the day watch in port—08:00 to 16:00 hours—and today we would be loading five million gallons of cargo JP-5 jet fuel for the fleet. The person-in-charge for dangerous liquids, or *PIC-DL,* is the Cargo Mate, in this case LAS; however, the Watch Officer also bears some responsibility. Most importantly, the Watch Officer must make certain no JP-5 is spilled, and if any overflows on deck, that all the scuppers or deck drains are plugged to prevent the petroleum product from going over the side into the pristine tropical waters...the key being the plugging of all scuppers. As the load out continued throughout the day,

I got a call on the radio from A/B Stanz, who is now acting as the Rover. I heard the crackling of the radio, "Hey, Mate on Watch. Rover here."

I dutifully reply, "Rover, Mate on Watch. Go ahead."

Stanz returns, "Mate on Watch, please call me at 7-3-2." As I was on the bridge at the time, correcting publications, I picked up the ship's internal dial telephone and dialed (yes, it's a rotary phone)...7-3-2.

Stanz picked up. "You better get down here. The Chief Mate is going around removing all the scupper plugs!"

Without even answering, I hung up the phone, with my eyes opened wide, and I flew down the ladderwell, as I grabbed my radio and belched, "Stanz, meet be at the aft end of the tank deck port side." With that I heard,"Roger."

I met Stanz at the after end of the tank deck, and it is on the tank deck, which as noted on the SHINNECOCK is the main deck, that the scuppers reside. In total there were twelve scuppers on the tank deck. Sure enough, I saw right away the Chief Mate had indeed removed the after scupper plugs. This is especially distressing, as there was quite a bit of rainwater accumulated on the after end of the tank deck from the previous evening's regular tropical thunderstorms. The problem arises in the fact that the tank deck is the working deck and the deck which includes all the tank tops, tanks vents, overflow discharge containment bins, and the like, which naturally lends itself to having some JP-5 residue on deck. Any water added to this residue that washed over the side would create an oil sheen on the water. Even the slightest sheen on the water constitutes an oil spill. When Chief Mate Borg unplugged the scuppers the rainwater, mixed with oily residue, was heading toward the aft scupper plugs on the port side of the ship. This was due to the vessel being trimmed astern and to the port side. Luckily, I raced down to the scupper quickly enough and, together with A/B Stanz, we re-plugged the scupper before the oil-infused rainwater could make its way over the side. Had I been just mere minutes late and the rainwater flowed out the unplugged scupper, a sheen most definitely would have appeared. As this would be considered an oil spill, many U.S. Navy, U.S. government, and Panamanian government agencies and officials would be sent into action. Any resultant negligence most certainly would fall to me in addition to LAS, and even Captain Stone. Our officer licenses and ability to make a living may very well have been negatively affected. Undoubtedly lucky, I witnessed firsthand Chief Mate Martin Borg's ruthlessness… and all over a woman.

That same evening we shifted to at sea watches at midnight, as we would be getting underway at 10:00 the next morning. As I was assigned the midnight to four at sea watch, I took over upon the shift from in port watches. At about 02:00, I was making a round of the ship, and decided to stop by the aft officers' lounge, located in the aft house. Recall there was also a forward officers' lounge in which I had to sleep my first night aboard due to my run-in with Bonnie. I walked into the aft lounge and the TV was on and, as I was pouring a cup of coffee, in rushed Chief Mate Borg, out of breadth, panting, and trying to spit out his words, "I got you… I got you…I caught you watching TV on watch. I'm gonna go right now and write you up."

Astonished, I looked at Borg and gently replied, "Mate, are you OK? You look like you're gonna have a heart attack."

Borg shot back as he departed the lounge, "When you're done with your watch, stop by my office to sign your disciplinary."

I just shook my head and my radio crackled, "Mate on Watch, this is Leter, please call the gangway."

I transmitted, "Roger." I picked up the dial telephone in the lounge and dialed 7-3-2.

Leter picked up, "Gangway, Leter here."

I began, "Mate on Watch. What's up?"

Leter explained, "I just saw the Chief Mate jump down from the pier onto a camel and then climb up the Jacobs ladder that was hanging there, and sorta snuck onboard."

Now it occurred to me what had just transpired, so I continued, "Leter, I know. He was just going nuts in the lounge…Thanks." Wow, I thought, Borg is certifiable, again my maxim is affirmed, that being "you must be a drunk or nuts to go to sea for a living." Clearly, Borg was the latter…wacko. In any case, I continued with my duties in preparation for getting underway in a few hours. Perched on the bridge tending to such duties, Captain Stone showed up. He appeared to be in an uncharacteristically good mood, for the Bulldog anyway, and beside it was 03:30 in the morning. Stone poured himself a cup of coffee and asked me how everything was going on my watch.

"Doing well, Captain. Please excuse me. I have to report to the Chief Mate's office."

The Bulldog looked at me with a somewhat puzzled expression and questioned, "Why would the Chief Mate want to see you at four AM? What can't wait until the morning?" So I proceeded in a matter-of-fact manner to explain the incident at the lounge.

"Well Captain, I was getting a cup of coffee in the aft lounge, and a winded Chief Mate burst into the room claiming I was watching TV and he would be writing me up and to see him at the end of my watch to sign the disciplinary."

Captain Stone's appearance transformed to red and I swear if it were possible, smoke would have emanated from his ears, he was so mad. He stomped off to the dial phone on the bridge and dialed what I can only assume was the Chief Mate, as I only heard his side of the conversation, "Mate, what the hell are you doing with this BS and the TV watching." There was a pause, as Borg must have tried to explain, but Captain Stone wouldn't let him proceed, "Marty, shut up and listen, cut this crap out. You're not writing anyone up, and in a second I'm gonna be writing someone up and his name starts with M." Stone slammed the handset into the receiver, almost knocking the phone off the bulkhead. He turned at me and barked, "It's all taken care of. Just continue on your watch. I'm going to my office." With that, the old Bulldog struck below, stomping like the elephant he is down the passageway. The story didn't quite end there for Borg and me. Marty and I would sail together one more time, albeit years later, when I was Master, and he was my Chief Mate.

It would be my first job as Master, and I picked up the ship in Sasebo, Japan. The ship was an *AFS,* or Auxiliary Fleet Support Ship, or affectionately referred to as an "Attack Food Ship." This ship was also an UNREP ship with a large crew, not unlike the SHINNECOCK. When I was assigned to the ship, I was told my Chief Mate was Borg. I thought, wow, that should be interesting. But, being the professional to which I espoused, I would give Borg the benefit of the doubt and start the assignment off fresh, no grudges held. I am certain when he heard my name as the new Master, he must have wanted to sink into his chair. For he knew how poorly he treated me when I was the young officer. When I met with Borg, it was all professional and proper. As it happened, I discovered Borg was very good at directing and managing the ship's maintenance and repair, but very uneasy on the bridge. That is sensible, as he probably had not stood a bridge watch in twenty years. As is normal practice entering or departing port, during UNREP, and most operations, the Chief Mate's position is to stand next to the Captain on the bridge, assisting as necessary. I could clearly see that Borg was very uncomfortable on the bridge during these evolutions. At these times, he would often ask me if he could go out on deck to manage something or another. I gladly permitted him to go as I knew he was uncomfortable and further, he was better served running the mariners locally vice from the bridge. After noting this phenomenon on several occasions, I decided to give Marty the choice if he would rather remain on deck for most operations. When I offered him this option, it was if I brightened his entire day. As it turned out, he was very appreciative. Over time, I also noted how well he and I got along as well as his performance. He executed his duties very well. Marty kept the ship in optimum material condition, he kept within budget, and his required tests, inspections, and training were all current. I started to enjoy working with Marty. In fact, when time for performance evaluations were due, I handed him an outstanding rating and noted his strengths.

Not long after Borg's evaluation was filed, I received a satellite call from the MSC Port Captain. In my neighborhood, the Port Captain position is akin to the *Capo dei capi* or *boss of bosses.* Essentially, he is in administrative charge of all the Masters on all the ships; he makes the assignments, he writes their evaluations, and the like. The Port Captain is normally a very senior MSC Master who, in addition to supervising all the Masters, is utilized as the Command's subject matter expert.

I picked up the satellite phone and the conversation unfolded as such. I dutifully proclaimed, "Hello, Captain. How may I be of assistance?" And of course, I heard my voice repeat, "Hello, Captain. How may I be of assistance…" In addition to the voice delay on the satellite phone, from time to time, I would often hear my own voice after the delay. It's quite annoying.

The Port Captain responded, "Doing well. Frankie, I just received Martin Borg's quarterly evaluation and I had to call you."

After the delay I acknowledged, "Really? Why is that, Captain?"

The Port Captain explained further, "You wrote a gleaming report on Borg. He has never had such a positive report. You don't mind having him as your Mate?" I countered proudly, "Captain, no, not at all. I would take Marty any day as my Mate. He has done an outstanding job."

The Port Captain returned with an astonishing proclamation, "OK, Frankie. You got him. From now on, I will send Borg as your Mate whenever he comes off vacation for a new hitch." And that was it. Let it be said, let it be done, forever more I had my own personal Chief Mate...Marty Borg. Who'd have thought such a thing, when he was screaming at me on SHINNECOCK.

CHAPTER FOURTEEN

"To be a winner you must associate with winners..."

- Rear Admiral Floyd H. "Hoss" Miller, USN (Ret.)

Superintendent

State University of New York

Maritime College at Ft. Schuyler

1982-1995

After we got underway that day from Rodman for our usual weeklong support of the fleet, I was on my afternoon watch and recalled I had not filled out my overtime sheet for this pay period. Overtime, colloquial known as *OT,* is everything to the mariner. On average, a mariner will double his annual base pay with overtime. As such, many a mariner relies on overtime to cover all his bills. This aberration would return to haunt me later in my career at sea, for I was warned by many a Captain to "learn to live on my base pay." The base pay was so minuscule, as compared to my commercial counterparts, that it was virtually impossible. On SHINNECOCK, my base pay was $21,819. If I doubled that with overtime, my annual salary was approximately $43,368, and with MSC that's based on working on the SHINNECOCK for the entire twelve months in the year. If I had secured either an *EXXON* or *ARCO* job out of Ft. Schuyler, my annual salary would have been $50,000 a year for twelve-hour days with no overtime. However, I would only have to work six months a year for that salary, altogether different from my compensation with MSC on SHINNECOCK.

As a Third Officer, I am authorized OT for all operational activities outside of my normal watches, either at sea or in port. Some of these evolutions include arrival and departure duties, UNREP duties, dinner relief for Second Mate Matt, fire and safety routine duties, and any duties assigned by either Chief Mate Dashman or Borg. Being on the midnight to four at sea watch provided me with copious OT as most operations events fall outside my duty hours. Upon completion of the two-week pay period, I would submit my OT sheet to the Chief Mate, and he would either approve or disapprove my submissions. Now Dashman never disapproved my OT, not that I was padding the numbers. But Borg would disapprove many an hour by what is referred to as *Red Lining*. This encompasses Borg taking a red pen and literally running a line through that particular OT entry. It bears repeating, red lining does not make a mariner happy. My OT rate on SHINNECOCK is $24.50 per hour. Rather compelling is the fact the Bosun's OT rate on SHINNECOCK is $28 per hour. Normally, for a non-officer, even one as senior as the Bosun, the OT rate is less than that of an officer. But this wasn't the case on SHINNECOCK. For me to have a higher OT rate than either Bosuns Pickle or Ramirez, I would have to be the Second Mate, receiving a whopping fifty-cent more per hour. It would be a severe understatement to say that managing overtime throughout my tenure at sea created some interesting adventures.

Years into my career, as Chief Mate, I received my first full taste of budgeting OT. Mariners are an interesting sort...especially in the area of OT. Most commonly the mariners hope and pray, and I mean literally kneeling with hands clasped, for the overtime duty to run past the hour. Not for an entire half an hour mind you, no, they look forward to as little as one to five minutes past the hour. That extra minute or so will provide the mariner with either an extra half an hour for non-officers or an extra hour for officers in OT pay...for essentially not working. I have had many a debate with numerous mariners as to whether or not the OT duty went one minute past the hour. Another instance in which the mariners are in OT ecstasy is, if by chance, the overtime runs past the hour and such hour is one of the meal hours. Now, not only will the mariner receive the extra hour or half an hour OT pay, they will also receive an additional hour pay due to the fact the OT slid into the meal hour. The mariners refer to this anomaly as a *plus one.* Simply, the *one* being the penalty hour pay for mealtime, even though these same mariners will also get an opportunity to actually eat their meal. The holy grail of OT aberrations occurs when an OT operation is *Stood Down,* vice being secured, and then *Re-Manned* within two hours. An example of the aforesaid exists when OT would be stood down at 12 noon and re-manned at 14:00. The OT clock would continue from 1200-1400 in addition to the plus one OT hour for mealtime.

I must note these OT exceptions only appear during operational overtime instances. By its very nature, routine overtime will not be performed through lunches, for only one minute or a few minutes after an hour, and during mealtimes. Routine OT includes maintenance and non-emergency repairs, upkeep, etc.

I recall a particular assignment on which I was sent to relieve a Master due to his fiscal mismanagement. Evidently, the ship's budget was one million dollars in the red...in the first quarter of the fiscal year. When I arrived, the Chief Engineer with whom I sailed as we advanced through the ranks, took me aside and explained the crew was out of control with abusing the overtime. Moreover, the Captain I had just relieved was totally complacent to this fact.

The ship was operating in the Western Pacific, or the WESTPAC, Area of Responsibility (AOR) and designated as a West Coast, Pacific, or simply an MSC PAC ship. This AOR encompassed the area from the California coast to the Far East, otherwise known as the U.S. Navy's Third and Seventh fleets. It was common knowledge throughout the MSC fleet, the ships deployed in WESTPAC, those being West Coast or MSC PAC ships, reported bloated overtime budgets. Meantime, the MSC ships operating in the Atlantic, Mediterranean, Northern Europe, or the Second, Fourth, and Sixth Fleets, referred to as East Coast, Atlantic, or MSC LANT ships, budgeted efficiently. The Fifth Fleet or Middle East AOR was serviced by both MSC PAC and MSC LANT ships. Further, for the most part MSC LANT ships ended the fiscal year in the black and, oddly, unlike MSC PAC ships, MSC LANT ships were held culpable for fiduciary acumen by MSC. This dichotomy was well-known to the upper echelon within MSC and unbelievably was accepted with no questions asked. Astonishingly, when such a disparagement in budget expenditures for performing the exact same mission would be discussed, the decision makers at MSC would quote the company line, "That's the cost of doing business in WESTPAC." Compelling was the fact MSC had dispatched me, a predominantly East Coast ship's Master, to relieve a WESTPAC ship in financial disarray. I didn't have to contemplate that fact very long, for prior to my assignment, the Port Captain specifically informed me the reason was specifically to bring the ship's budget in line and stop the abuse of overtime. I guess an MSC decision maker finally noted the disparagement between the West Coast and East Coast MSC ships, and had a grand plan to finally reign in the economic fraud, waste, and abuse.

After my arrival on the ship and my discussion with the Chief Engineer, I performed a forensic audit of the ship's budget. Granted, I am no CPA, but I knew enough when the numbers didn't add up. Ostensibly, I did not need to dig too deeply into the financials, as the abuse appeared in my face. The first was something called *pre-overtime,* obviously, a new term of which I was not aware, sarcasm emphasized. The day workers or those with duty hours 08:00-17:00, in the various departments, would submit overtime for work before they even started working for the day...unbelievable.

My next discovery dealt with the outright scam when it came to fraudulent port costs—in particular, the renting of vehicles for the ship whilst in port. Prior to arriving in port, the ship transmits an official Naval Message called a *LOGREQ,* or Logistic Requirements. Recall, MSC CLF ships are designated *USNS,* for U.S. Naval Ship, as bona fide Naval assets, and utilize the same supply and messaging protocol as the warfighting ships. A LOGREQ message notifies all involved parties, such as the Naval base, the ship's husbanding agent, the tugboats, the harbor and/or docking pilots, the ship's chandler, and the like of the specific requirements the ship will need during the entire stay in port. One "request for services" line deals with the renting of vehicles. On an East Coast MSC ship, the LOGREQ normally requests two vehicles, a pickup truck and a sedan. The pickup truck is primarily needed to ferry mail and small items to the post office and supply areas; the sedan is used for crew medical appointments as well as any crew change out. This appears as a justifiable expense. However, on this West Coast MSC ship, when the LOGREQ was brought to me for the final approval, I was stunned. Under "vehicles," the Supply Officer requested twelve. Unbelievably, he wanted one sedan for the Captain along with one sedan for each department head to include the Chief Engineer, Supply Officer, Sparks, Medical Officer, Purser, Mildept OIC, Air detachment OIC, and the 1st Engineer. The LOGREQ even requested a vehicle dedicated to the Watch Officer, which makes no sense as the Watch Officer is on duty...on the ship. These vehicles were in addition to a pickup truck and a five-ton stake truck as well. Moreover, the Supply Officer requested the Captain's vehicle come with a driver to chauffeur the Captain. Interestingly enough, this was not a foreign port, rather it was a U.S. port, where crew could easily go to any rental agency on the pier for a car, if they so choose. Altogether, the expense for these vehicles was not only extravagant—it was borderline graft.

The next abuse I discovered onboard this crooked ship fell to *Sparks'* overtime or abuse of such. I discovered that he would submit two OT hours and a plus one, overtime entry from 06:00-08:00…everyday!

I called him into the office to question this, "What's the daily entry from 06:00-08:00 for three hours, called reading messages?"

Sparks confidently answered, "Well, Captain, I read all the messages and have them ready for you when you awake and go to work."

I looked up from my desk and explained, "Sparks, a couple of things. First, I awake at 04:00, not 08:00; second, we are one day ahead of the Base back East; third and finally, I can certainly wait until after the workday starts for my messages."

Clearly despondent, Sparks sheepishly replied, "That was the way Captain O'Malley wanted it."

Exasperated, I responded, "Well, there is a new Sheriff in town. You are no longer authorized three hours every morning to read messages." With that, Sparks departed my office. The fact of the matter was, even if I authorized three hours of OT, I would maybe get 30 minutes of actual work. Think about it, Sparks puts in for three hours from 06:00-08:00. One of those hours is a meal hour, so he automatically gets a free hour OT pay for not working. Next, as an officer, he is authorized thirty minutes to get up and get to work for any OT, paid mind you, as this is his *callout.* Doing the calculations, at 06:00 Sparks starts his overtime clock, he wakes, showers, dresses, and reports to the radio room at 06:30. He reads messages from 06:30 to 06:45 and then exits the radio room and makes his way down to the saloon for breakfast. He meanders through the decks arriving at 07:00 for breakfast. At this point, he sits down and is waited upon and spends the next thirty minutes leisurely eating in the Saloon. At 07:30 he migrates from the saloon, one would surmise, back to the radio room as Sparks is on overtime, but this is not to be; rather, Sparks walks with purpose to his stateroom for he must use the head. He finally arrives back in the radio room at his desk and the time is 07:50, where he does actual overtime work for ten more minutes. Tabulated, Sparks performed exactly twenty-five minutes of actual work but was paid for three full hours.

Now that, being rather fraudulent, compared nothing to the Chief Mate working, or not working the thirty or so A/B day workers on straight time, thus leaving the bulk of the work for overtime.

It would be almost comical if not true. A typical day for the Chief Mate and the A/B's on this West Coast MSC ship started with a muster at 08:00. They would gather, and then for the next fifteen minutes, the Chief Mate would speak with the day workers and then he would depart to his office. From 08:15 to 08:30 the Bosun would then speak with the day workers and assign each their jobs for the day. From 08:30 to 08:45 the day worker A/B's would meander to the tool locker, paint locker, or what-have-you and arrive at their job. From 08:45 to 09:30 or for some forty-five minutes, they would perform actual physical labor. From 09:30 to 09:45, the day workers would stop working, pick themselves up, clean up, and stroll to the lounge for their union mandated AM *coffee break*. Officially there are two required coffee breaks for day workers onboard the ships, 10:00-10:15 in the morning, and 15:00-15:15 in the afternoon. The key being *officially*, as noted, the day workers arrived at coffee not at 10:00 but rather fifteen minutes early at 09:45. They sit back, relax, maybe even kickback their filthy boots on the coffee table for the next forty-five minutes and ramble around for fifteen minutes, arriving back on the job at 11:00. From 11:00 to 11:15 the day workers are affecting actual labor. At 11:15, the day workers stop working, saunter back to the tool locker or paint locker and return their equipment used in the morning. Next, they drift at snail's pace to the crew mess and are seated, waiting to be served, by 11:30. Interestingly enough, the meal hour for day workers does not commence until noon, but that is evidently just a technicality. The day workers then engage in *eat-it and beat-it,* scarfing down their lunch so as to be in their rack by 11:45 for the requisite "nooner" or nap. Adding up the numbers for the morning work, the day workers were paid for four hours of work, but in reality only completed one hour of substantive work. In the afternoon, the lack of work is just as egregious. The day workers muster at 13:00 and are a little more spry arriving with tools and/or paint at their workstation by 13:15. The day workers are hard at work for one and a quarter hours. At this point, they stop, place their tools or paint brush down, perk up, clean up, and slowly cruise to afternoon coffee break, again arriving fifteen minutes early at 14:45. The day workers enjoy themselves a little less in the afternoon, this time for thirty minutes and are back on the job a bit later at 15:45. Real work continues for thirty minutes. Promptly at 16:15, the day workers stop working, as if a work whistle had sounded, return their tools, paint, brushes, and cleanup. Next, they amble and loiter about, arriving in the crew mess hall at 17:00 sharp for the evening meal. Adding the afternoon work numbers, I arrive at one hour and forty-five minutes production, which is much improved than the lone hour of work in the morning. In total, for eight hours pay, the ship received approximately two hours and forty-five minutes of fruitful labor. Oh, but the day is not over. On this fraud-laden ship, at 17:30 the same day workers would *turn to* for overtime of three hours…every day. By only accomplishing a pittance of work during the straight time workday, the Chief Mate would then use the excuse for OT as credulous to complete whatever work remaining unfinished.

Overtime does not necessarily imply the mariners are employed at a furious pace. Yes, those mariners on OT are held to a higher standard of job production just by nature of almost triple pay. Nevertheless, I have witnessed mariners on OT, well, doing anything but working. When I was Chief Mate on an *AOE, or Auxiliary Ship Oiler (tanker) and Explosives (ammunition),* my mentor Captain and I were walking the decks. All of sudden, he stopped, turned his head and, without saying a word, motioned for me to look down on the UNREP deck. I followed his finger with my eyes as he pointed and, to my utter amazement at what I was witnessing, my jaw dropped. Plainly, there was an A/B sitting down, with his boots off, and his socks removed as well. Incredibly, he was cutting his toenails…on overtime! Oh, it didn't end there. The Captain climbed down to the UNREP deck, with me in tow, looked at the A/B, said not a word to him, but rather picked up all the nail clippings off the deck.

When he was finished with that task, he turned, looked at me and directed, "Hold out your hands." Without saying a word in reply, I reluctantly cupped my hands together and held them forward toward the Captain. He then placed all the A/B's nasty nail clippings in my hands and commented, "I trust you'll handle this." I said nothing, but rather stood there for a moment as the Captain turned, climbed up the ladderwell and headed off to his office. The damage was clearly done.

It would be a cold day in hell before the Captain would authorize non-discretionary overtime for the A/B's. My next move: contact Bosun Ramirez to meet me at the UNREP shop. When he arrived at the door to the shop, I was waiting with my hands still cupped holding the A/B's funky nail clippings. I repeated the series of events leading to which the Captain had just assigned me minutes earlier.

I spoke,"Bosun, hold out your hands." He dutifully complied and I then turned my cupped hands over above his open hands and in fell the A/B's nail clippings.

Almost instinctively, Bosun Ramirez pulls his hands away and the nail clippings fell helplessly to the deck of the UNREP shop. Meantime, the Bosun barked out, "Mate, what is this crap?"

I matter-of-factly responded, "That's Miller's nail clippings which the Captain picked up after watching him cut them on OT." With a now concerned look in his eye, the Bosun returned with, "Mate, sorry about that, I will take care of it and you won't have any trouble with him anymore."

Nodding my head in agreement, I spoke a final comment on the subject, "Bosun, you take care of Miller and I will smooth things over with the Old Man about the OT."

Returning to filling out my OT on that clear afternoon onboard SHINNECOCK, A/B Stanz walked onto the bridge from his lookout post on the starboard wing and reported, "Hey Mate, I got a contact, broad on the starboard bow, hull up, looks to be DIW." To the land-lubber that sentence probably sounds like some sort of gibberish but broken down into its parts actually provides quite a bit of information.

First, a *contact* is an object on the water. It could be a vessel, land, rocks, shoals, discolored water, buoys, beacons, lighthouses, floating objects or similar which may be of interest to the Watch Officer. Most importantly, a contact must be investigated, especially if there is any risk of collision.

The second coded information in the sentence, *broad on the starboard bow,* refers to relative bearings by points...thirty-two points of exactly eleven and a quarter degrees, to be more precise. Starting on the bow moving aft around the starboard side:

DEAD AHEAD – ONE POINT ON THE STARBOARD BOW – TWO POINTS ON THE STARBOARD BOW – THREE POINTS ON THE STARBOARD BOW – BROAD ON THE STARBOARD BOW – THREE POINTS FORWARD OF THE STARBOARD BEAM – TWO POINTS FORWARD OF THE STARBOARD BEAM – ONE POINT FORWARD OF THE STARBOARD BEAM – ON THE STARBOARD BEAM — ONE POINT ABAFT OF THE STARBOARD BEAM – TWO POINTS ABAFT OF THE STARBOARD BEAM – THREE POINTS ABAFT OF THE STARBOARD BEAM – BROAD ON THE STARBOARD QUARTER – THREE POINTS ON THE STARBOARD QUARTER – TWO POINTS ON THE STARBOARD QUARTER – ONE POINT ON THE STARBOARD QUARTER – DEAD ASTERN.

Similarly, when starting on the bow moving aft down the port side, the only change is the side of the ship from starboard to port, otherwise the point system remains the same. The use of point system of relative bearings for contact identification is the preferred method for the U.S. Merchant Marine. Conversely, the U.S. Navy uses relative bearings in degrees, as in 360 degrees of a circle. The point system is much more user friendly and more accurate when passing contact information, especially when waking the Captain from a deep sleep to report a possible close quarters situation. Recall, the Merchant Marine are professional mariners, that's what we do better than anyone in the world, whereas the Navy are the warfighters. Think of the disparity of the two contact reporting methods. A Master, awakened out of a deep sleep with the words *contact two points on the starboard bow,* doesn't need to recall or calculate the actual ship's heading and course to know the approximate location of the contact in relation to his ship and any possible need for positive action. Inasmuch as a Navy ship Commanding Officer, or *CO,* awakened to the words, *target eighteen degrees to starboard,* requires some considerable thought in comparison to the Master. The CO must directly recall knowing the current heading of the vessel, then add the eighteen degrees to the true heading, and finally create a virtual picture of the situation instantly so as to correctly assess any need for positive action. Needless to say, that is quite a stretch for any human being roused from a deep REM sleep.

The third piece of information included in A/B Stanz report, *hull up*, describes the contact's location in relation to the horizon. Hull up indicates the contact is above the horizon and when viewed the horizon is beyond the contact, thus informing the fact the contact is closer than the horizon. *Hull down* illustrates the contact is below the horizon, or further off. The contact being below the horizon only permits viewing of the ship's superstructure, masts, or kingposts. *On the horizon*, is just that, the contact is sitting directly on the horizon line.

The fourth item in Stanz's report, *DIW*, correlates to the initials for *Dead In the Water.* Simply, the contact is not moving. This may be due to several factors, ranging from a mechanical failure to a fire to something as elementary as just drifting.

After Stanz delivered his lookout report, I stopped what I had been doing, pivoted and followed Stanz out the starboard wing blast watertight door. Stanz then pointed at the contact, at which time I used the gyro repeater with alidade affixed to shoot a bearing of the contact. Next, I picked up my binoculars to take a look at the contact. The horizon, being a clear day, was crisp and about twelve miles out, which put this contact at about ten miles off our starboard side. I wanted a better look; I turned around and climbed up the ladder to the signal bridge. I dashed over to the big eyes on the starboard side of the signal bridge. Peering through the lenses I could easily make out the contact as a *cigarette-type* ocean speedboat. The ultra-fast craft measured about sixty feet, and smoke was emitting from stern exhaust on the transom.

Not smoke as in a fire, but more of an exhaust type smoke. The peculiarity was the fact the boat was dead in the water.

I climbed back down to the starboard bridge wing and then strode onto the bridge. No sooner did I enter the bridge when I heard the VHF bridge-to-bridge radio squawking on channel sixteen, the international VHF hailing and emergency frequency.

"Mayday, Mayday, Mayday… this is ocean yacht *Bluewind.* We need assistance. Our engines are blown…Mayday, Mayday, Mayday…" Instinct directed me to the dial phone on the aft bulkhead behind the ship's telemotor wheel. I dial Captain Stone and relayed the distress call, "Captain, we are getting a distress call from a yacht on the starboard beam. Shall I acknowledge and start heading in their direction?"

The Bulldog shot back, "Start heading to the vessel. Do not say the name of our ship when you acknowledge them. Don't forget we are operating with the fleet. Then contact Commander Moore to pass on the information to the Fleet Commander."

I responded with an emphatic, "Yes Sir," and quickly followed by repeating his orders, then hanging up the phone. The prudent mariner will always repeat the orders of his superior, the reason being threefold. First, by repeating the orders, the supervisor will know he is understood. Second, it reinforces the order to the mariner, and third, anyone in the vicinity will also hear the superior's order.

I commanded the helmsman, "Right ten degrees rudder."

A/B Waddams, the helmsman at the time acknowledged, "Right ten degrees rudder, aye."

I sprinted over to the chart and calculated the course needed to intercept the distressed vessel and barked out, "Steady on course zero nine five."

Waddams, returned the order, "Rudder is ten degrees right coming to zero nine five, aye."

Next, I bolted to the EOT and rang up a slow ahead bell. Immediately, I saw the engine room acknowledge the speed change.

I picked up the VHF radio and transmitted on channel sixteen, "Mayday, Mayday, Mayday, Yacht *Bluewind*, this is the vessel on your port beam heading to you to provide assistance. Please standby for further instructions… Mayday, Mayday, Mayday…" I was careful not to mention the name of our ship or the fact we were a U.S. Naval Ship, for I understood we are operating with the Carrier and her position is always highly guarded. I also remembered from my training to repeat *Mayday* three times at the start and ending of every voice transmission with a vessel in distress. The purpose of which is to help keep the network clear of any extraneous transmissions as well as alert all vessels in the vicinity.

The *Bluewind* replied, "Mayday, Mayday, Mayday…this is Yacht *Bluewind*. We are standing by for instructions…Mayday, Mayday, Mayday…"

I turned just in time for Captain Bulldog to enter the bridge with his usual bravado, opening the door with such force it almost tore it from its hinges. Stone, dressed in his customary uniform or lack thereof, barked out, "I have the conn."

Now a prudent Master, barring an emergency to the ship, would assess the situation, speak with his Watch Officer, and then announce to the bridge watch team he had taken the conn, but I am speaking of Captain Blockhead himself, prudent seamanship be damned. When mentioning *the conn*, I'm referring to the officer who is directly responsible for controlling all of the ship's movements, the safe navigation of the vessel, and the safety of the crew and cargo. Normally, this individual is the Watch Officer, thus the detailed, specific, and regulated turnover process as discussed. The one qualifier in referencing the conn is that of the Master's authority. By nature of the fact the Master is in overall Command of the vessel and her operations, he may take the conn without any turnover; in fact, he may take the conn anytime for any reason, without notice. The Master will normally delineate such in his Standing Orders. However, I have seen, although rare, some Master's Standing Orders delineate that the moment the Master steps onto the bridge, he automatically has the conn. I don't necessarily agree with this extreme. There is ample concern for the creation of a link in the error chain if the Master simply assumes the conn without any information. Think about it, the Master has not had the opportunity to check the traffic situation, the radar picture, confirm the ship's position, nor allow his eyes to adjust for proper night vision, yet he takes the conn.

Stone started giving orders to the helm, making fine adjustments to the ship's course to intercept the vessel in distress. Meanwhile, I assumed my role as assisting the Master.

I proceeded to the dial phone once again on the aft bulkhead and dialed 7-6-2, the number for CDR Moore. The phone rang once, twice, and on the third ring, the Commander picked up, "Commander Moore."

I quickly replied, "We have a vessel in distress about ten miles off to starboard and the Captain wants you to notify Fleet Command."

Moore responded, "Roger, will do. Are we heading to assist?"

I continued the conversation, "Yes, the Captain is on the bridge now and we are heading toward the vessel in distress. Thanks," and with that, I hung up the phone.

"Call out the rescue boat team to standby and rouse the Chief Mate," the Bulldog screamed from out on the bridge wing.

I picked up the ship's public address microphone, which incidentally is mounted adjacent to the dial phone on the after bulkhead, and announced, "This is a callout for the rescue boat team. All rescue boat team members report to your stations and contact the bridge when manned and ready." Next, I picked up the UHF walkie-talkie radio clipped on my hip, brought the radio to my mouth, keyed the microphone, and called, "Chief Mate, Bridge. Your presence is requested on the bridge."

The speaker yelped, "Bridge, Chief Mate here, I'm on my way up."

I turned and looked out on the bridge wing and, sure enough, the Chief Mate had just climbed the ladder and was talking with the Old

Man. So I raced over to the radar, placed my head inside the darkening hood, used the analog dial for the variable range marker, or *VRM,* to ascertain the distance to the vessel in distress.

I then raised my head, and loudly bellowed, "Contact six miles out," at which point I saw Captain Stone on the bridge wing beckoning for me to come out. I did as directed, and as I was walking out the starboard bridge wing, the Chief Mate had commenced heading down on deck.

Stone fired back at me, "Call the vessel and tell them we will be making our approach on their port side and for them standby for lines."

I obediently answered, "Roger," and raced back to the VHF radio to relay the message to *Bluewind.* In the interim, the Chief Mate, Bosun, and the deck department day workers were preparing to take the vessel alongside so we may provide assistance. Lines were faked out on deck, fenders were deployed over the side, and engineers were standing by to take a look at the blown engine.

At the same time, Second Mate Matt walked up the bridge to see what was all the commotion. He asked,"What's going on up here?"

I proceeded to fill Matt in on all the happenings in regard to the vessel in distress, after which he walked out on the starboard bridge wing to talk to the Old Man. Matt then returned to the bridge, checked the radar, the chart, the helm, all of the items he would monitor if taking a watch, then without a word, he returned to the starboard bridge wing with the Captain. I walked over to the chart to plot a running fix, advancing *LAN,* or *Local Apparent Noon,* with the two sun lines I had shot during the course of my watch, adjusting our *DR,* or *Dead Reckoning,* plot accordingly.

With that my ear's perked up at Matt's voice stating, "Second Mate has the conn."

In almost unison the helmsman and I respond, "Second Mate has the conn, aye." I started to think, why would Matt take the conn since the Master had the conn? Immediately it hit me, of course, Captain Moron himself was not capable of conducting the necessary maneuvers to bring SHINNECOCK alongside the vessel in distress. To save face, Stone probably asked Matt to wrangle the ship into position, while he fabricated some excuse. In all my time onboard SHINNECOCK, I never really witnessed Stone tend to any of the actual ship handling himself.

As my mind was contemplating Stone's motives, I heard the command from Matt, "Dead slow ahead on both engines."

I rushed over to the EOT and rang up "dead slow ahead" on both engines. Practically instantly, the engine room answered on their EOT…dead slow ahead on both engines. From this point, I stayed put next to the helmsman and the EOT, ready to relay engine orders while simultaneously monitoring the helmsman in anticipation of the litany of helm orders as Matt brought us alongside the *Bluewind.*

In no time at all, Matt deftly and smartly maneuvered the massive SHINNECOCK alongside the tiny *Bluewind* sitting dead in the water. Matt was impressive and I had to sit back and smile, because he was my *big brother* upperclassman back at Ft. Schuyler. Next, I heard the UHF walkie-talkie radio squawking and crackling between the Chief Mate, Bosun, and the Captain. The lines were passed to the *Bluewind,* and the deck day workers were making the vessel fast against the fenders. All seemed to be normal for the situation, but then a blast flew from the walkie-talkie and it sounded like the Chief Mate, "Captain, you may want to call out a security alert. It looks like this boat is filled with pot!"

Stone never answered the Chief Mate; rather, he picked up the public address microphone on the starboard bridge wing and commanded, "Security Alert, Security Alert, Security Team to the starboard UNREP deck!" Cargo Mate LAS and the designated deck day workers trained as security immediately went into action, mustering at the armory, donning flak jackets, helmets and, most importantly, arms and ammunition, then raced to the starboard UNREP deck. It must have been quite a site from the drug smugglers' point of view. Thinking they were going to be rescued, only to look up and see 12 gun barrels pointed down on them.

What happened next could have been a scene out of any cop movie. The four crewmembers, or drug smugglers, were brought aboard SHINNECOCK, restrained with Zip-ties, examined by the medical officer, then locked in an empty ventilated storeroom with a guard at the door. Commander Moore notified the Carrier, and a helicopter was deployed to pick up the detainees. Captain Stone ordered the Chief Mate to load the *Bluewind* on deck. The Bosun and day workers topped and spotted the booms for a Burton rig or married falls, crafted a bridle and slings, and hoisted the *Bluewind* right out of the water and placed her on a set of cradles on the UNREP deck. Next, with the Cargo Mate and security team standing by, the day workers proceeded to offload fifty bales of marijuana…fifty! They stacked the bales on deck like a mountain of dope. Pictures were shot with the security team standing in front of pot mountain, as if they were fishermen standing for a photo with their catch.

I heard this and thought, I have to get in on this. By this time, Captain Stone had since departed the bridge to head down on deck to take charge locally. Matt remained on the bridge with the conn, holding us in position, steaming with bare steerageway.

I took a shot and asked Matt if I could run down on deck for a quick photo. Matt looked at me, and with his dry sense of humor, commented, "OK, Crockett, go ahead and get in on the glory," a clear reference to the 80's police drama, *Miami Vice*. With the photo session completed, the drug booty was inventoried and photographed and then each bale hauled up to the signal shack under heavy security team guard. Finally the loot was locked inside the signal shack with a trace-able metal seal and with an armed sentry standing watch. Now, where would Big Red stand her watch as the signal bridge was secured? Oh no, probably on the navigation bridge with me…Yikes…

In the end we dropped off the drugs with the *DEA,* or U.S. Drug Enforcement Agency, at Naval Station Rodman. They were waiting on the pier with trucks, black sedans, and oodles of armed agents. As for the smugglers themselves, they were picked up by the helo from the Carrier and, I may only assume, eventually transferred to the DEA and held for prosecution. All that remained from our adventure was the yacht *Bluewind.* The DEA had no use for the craft; as such, we offloaded the *Bluewind* from our ship to a flatbed trailer and it actually wound up at the Rodman base marina. My only guess is that the Navy kept the *Bluewind* for recreational use by those stationed at Rodman. Of course, there is the matter of the blown engine on *Bluewind*, oh well.

CHAPTER FIFTEEN

"A ship is not a ship when she sits alongside the pier..."

- CAPT James Di Simonne

Master, *T.S. Empire State VI*

Commandant of Cadets

State University of New York

Maritime College at Ft. Schuyler

1986-1992

After eight months operating out of Naval Station Rodman in the Panama Canal Zone, the Good Ship SHINNECOCK headed back to her home port at the big Naval base on the Elizabeth River in Norfolk, Virginia.

The phone rang… I jumped out of my rack, almost floating to my desk, and picked up the phone. "Third Mate."

I could then hear Matt's voice, "Drop your cocks and grab your socks. It's 07:00. This is your callout. We are making our approach to Chesapeake light. See you on the bridge at 07:30. Oh, and don't forget to wear your hat."

Excitedly I blurted out, "Roger, will do… see you in a few," and then I hung up the phone. I drew back the curtains on my porthole and opened the deadlight cover and could see it was a clear late January day. I knew it was rather chilly, as the deck was cold when my feet hit the floor tiles—a sure sign of the change of weather from the tropics to the mid-Atlantic.

I was so excited about returning to the U.S. that I didn't bother going to eat breakfast. I had butterflies in my stomach, I was so thrilled. As for the hat to which Matt was referring, all the Deck Officers and the Captain bought Panama hats when we were in Panama to specifically wear upon arrival in Norfolk. Granted the Panama hats were not part of our regulation uniform, but even Commander Moore, our senior Naval officer aboard, thought it was appropriate, given our eight-month deployment.

When I arrived on the bridge to take my place next to the helmsman and operate the EOT, I noticed everyone was in his best uniform. I was in utter amazement when I looked at Captain Bulldog, for he was actually in some semblance of a regulation uniform…even sans stains. The Bulldog actually looked presentable, and yes, he too donned his Panama hat.

So here we were making our way to the pilot station, CAPT Stone, Second Mate Matt, and Chief Mate Borg all wearing our Panama hats on the bridge. On the bow, Cargo Mate LAS with his Panama hat, the ship's Bosun Pickle and the anchor detail were stationed, as well. At the pilot ladder awaiting the pilot boat stood Chips and two A/B day workers. Borg turned, stared right at me and barked, "Go down to the pilot ladder and get the pilot."

I obediently replied, "Yes Sir," and with that, I departed the bridge and started making my way down to the jungle deck to the pilot ladder to await the pilot boarding. It is law that a Licensed Officer be present when the pilot is boarding or departing, as well as to escort said pilot to and from the bridge.

When I arrived at the pilot ladder, I saw the pilot boat making its approach to come alongside on our port side. I unclipped my UHF walkie-talkie radio from my belt, brought the microphone to my mouth and relayed, "Bridge, it looks like the pilot boat is making her approach."

Matt answered, "Bridge. Aye."

I poked my head over the rail as Chips and the A/B's stood by and I relayed to the bridge, "Pilot's on the ladder."

Matt answered, "Pilot on the ladder. Aye."

No sooner did I receive Matt's acknowledgement than I had to transmit one final time, "Pilot aboard and pilot boat away. We're on our way up."

Matt returned, "Time 08:00 pilot aboard. Aye."

With that, I escorted the pilot up to the bridge.

Of course, the pilot had to comment on the choice of my headwear, "I see y'all must be coming back from the Caribbean."

I shot back, "Panama, to be exact."

The pilot has an ah-ha moment and remarks, "Right…Panama, so the hats, I get it…clever."

I finished our short conversation with, "Wait until you see everyone on the bridge." The pilot nodded and then I opened the door from the chart room to the bridge and introduced the pilot to CAPT Stone, but not before I offered a cup of coffee to him, "How do you take your coffee, Mr. Pilot?"

He mumbled, "Black, please."

Part of my job as Third Officer is to offer and serve the pilot coffee upon his arrival on the bridge.

At this point, Matt instructed me to go to after steering and relieve Third Mate Rob, so that he could take his station on the bridge. After all, his underway watch runs from 08:00 to 12:00. Regardless who has the conn, the designated Watch Officer should be on the bridge, at the very least, to keep the logbook. I took my leave of the bridge with one last look and, in the distance, I could see the twenty-three-mile Chesapeake Bay Bridge Tunnel, or *CBBT.* That's a sure sign that we are almost home. However, for me, the sight of the CBBT is rather new, as I have only been to Norfolk once in my life. That one time was for an intercollegiate sailing regatta held at Old Dominion University a few years back when I was a *Mug* at Ft. Schuyler. A Mug is a freshman acronym for Midshipman Under Guidance.

In no time at all I trekked back to after steering and there was Rob nodding off while sitting on his makeshift boiler-chemical-can-seat. I walked up to him with the low din of the steering engine grinding in the background and tapped him on the shoulder,"Hey Rob, go up to the bridge, OK?"

He groggily replied, with a big yawn, "Yeah sure… where are we anyway?"

I updated him, "We picked up the pilot and we are heading toward the CBBT."

Rob perked up, "Wow, that's great, I'll be home for afternoon drinks."

As he departed, I took my position at the after steering conning station, albeit remaining standing. I looked to my left, and who should I see sitting on his makeshift seat, but A/B Corastas, but this time thankfully without his warped sketchpad. Rather, Corastas remained seated, wearing his well-known scowl and a sound-powered phone headset over his ears, in the event the bridge called. I should have been pleased for, at the very least, he was awake…but not alert…that was certain.

At approximately 09:00, the sound-powered phone squawked, the bell rang, and the light flashed as Corastas answered via his headset and microphone. He repeated the command loud enough for me to understand over racket that is after steering, "Roger. Send the Third Mate up to the fantail and have him check in on the radio when he gets there." That was my cue. I immediately departed after steering, climbed the ladderwell to the fantail, turned around and I was out on deck at the after mooring station.

Almost simultaneously I heard the following announcement over the public address system, "Deck department day workers *fore and aft.*" This signals the specific A/B's, BM's, Bosuns, and Officers whose duty is tying up the ship to report to their stations either on the bow, or *fore,* or on the fantail, or *aft.* As I walked aft to the *transom,* or the most after structure of the hull, the part with the ship's name embossed, I started to notice a gaggle of day workers starting to arrive.

I unclipped my radio from my belt and blurted, "Bridge, this is the stern. Radio check."

This time I heard Borg's marbled mouth, "Stern…bridge. I read you *Lima Charlie,*" code for Loud and Clear. This period at the end of the voyage is very precarious, as we are so close to home, but there is always that chance that could change. Yes, such a situation had actually occurred to me a few years later on another ship. The ship was another UNREP ship, a new build, and we were returning after an eight-month deployment to the Mediterranean Sea, not unlike the SHINNECOCK returning from her eight-month deployment. Also similar, I was on the fantail in my position as the officer in charge of the stern mooring detail with the mooring details fore and aft. Moreover, the ship was just about ready to cross the Hampton Roads Bridge Tunnel, spitting distance from the Naval base piers. All of a sudden the ship commences turning around, right in the middle of the channel. The A/B day workers, the UNREP Bosun and I were confused, for this has never happened and furthermore, we were so close to home we could literally see the piers.

With that, I quickly got on the radio and called the bridge, "Bridge… Stern here, what is going on? We seem to be turning?"

As I am transmitting my question to the bridge, all the men gathered around to hear the response, "Stern…Bridge. We just got the call to turn around and head back to the Med. Next stop…Rota, Spain."

I looked up and witnessed grown men fraught and in tears, none of whom saying a word. I answered the bridge, "Roger, heading back to the Med," my voice trailing off at the end of my acknowledgement. Then it was as if the bridge awakened a sleeping lion with the mooring detail A/B's starting to get riled up, yelling louder and louder. I started trying to calm down the detail, telling all there must be a national security reason to turn us around. With the entire hullabaloo, I failed to notice one particular A/B leave the fantail, and at this point we did not secure the fore and aft mooring details.

I start to walk athwartships looking for this A/B, when out of the blue, I hear, "There he is…he's in his Gumby suit." Sure enough, I peered off to the starboard side of the fantail and there was A/B Walsh decked out in his *Gumby* suit. Better known as a survival suit or immersion suit, it is a special type of buoyant waterproof dry suit, characterized with built-in feet and hood to protect the mariner from hypothermia in the water after abandoning ship in the open seas. Hence the name, Gumby, as the suit's appearance resembles the 1970's child's toy and television program. Immersion suits were mandated after the *Marine Electric* disaster of February 1983 in which thirty-one crew members perished due to hypothermia.

I ran over to Walsh and bellowed, "Walsh, what are you doing?" Walsh is a rather lanky fellow and stands about six foot eight inches tall, has a clubfoot, which in itself is interesting, but I can't imagine how difficult it must have been for him to donn a Gumby suit with such a deformity.

Walsh shouted back at me, "Mate, I can't take it anymore, I can't go back to the Med. I can't do it. I am out of here…"

With that, Walsh leapt over the side of the ship and started a modified elementary backstroke toward the beach. For a second Walsh looked so peaceful, gently moving his arms as his Gumby suit kept him on the surface; however, I quickly regained the realization of the man overboard and called on the radio, "Bridge…stern here. A/B Walsh just jumped over the side of the ship. He put on his Gumby suit and jumped off…"

The bridge responded, "Stern…Bridge. Roger, copy all, looks like the escort boat is going to fish him out of the water." Sure enough, our Navy security escort boat picked Walsh out of the water. I was informed later when the escort boat called the ship so as to transfer Walsh back aboard, the Captain advised them not to bother, and to drop Walsh off with the authorities with the charge of desertion.

Intentionally jumping ship was not entirely new to me. I experienced it first hand during my first hitch aboard SHINNECOCK with A/B DiNapoli, later with A/B Walsh, and a third time with O/S Blaine. I was Second Mate on another UNREP ship, an oiler, specifically, one of the new builds at that; we were operating off the coast of Virginia and North Carolina with the Fleet, referred to in Navy speak as the *VACAPES* area. It was about 04:30 and the Ordinary Seaman, O/S Blaine, had not arrived on watch at 03:45 as was his duty hours. After forty-five minutes, I asked one of the A/B's to go roust Blaine out of his rack. About ten minutes later, as I was working on the chart in the chartroom, O/S Blaine appeared. As it was somewhat private, I took Blaine to the side and asked, "Blaine, what is going on? It's a quarter to five and you're just now coming up to watch?"

Blaine looked at me and said, "I can't take it anymore...I can't take it anymore," and then ran out to the bridge.

I followed him on his heels, but he kept running and ran right out to the port bridge wing; in one fell swoop he dove off the bridge wing into the water. He looked like an Olympic diver the way he vaulted himself over the rail. I was dumbfounded, as the bridge wing was ninety feet off the water and the ship was making twelve knots. I yelled, "Man overboard port side...hard left rudder...sound the signal."

On the bridge the A/B rang off the "Oscar" signal on the ship's whistle delineating a man overboard. Meanwhile, I conducted a round turn, contacted the engine room, deployed the smoke float from the bridge wing, contacted the Captain and the Chief Mate, and commenced the man overboard protocol. In the end, we actually found O/S Blaine not ten minutes later and brought him aboard. As it turned out, O/S Blaine was illiterate and he could not read the change of the watch bill, which required his arrival on watch at 03:45, hence the reason he was tardy. There is no way I would have known that in a million years. Evidently my hypothesis continued to ring true: either you are an alcoholic or mentally unbalanced to go to sea for a living. Clearly, O/S Blaine was the latter.

The SHINNECOCK proceeded up the Thimble Shoals Channel, over the Chesapeake Bay Bridge Tunnel and continuing down over the Hampton Roads Bridge Tunnel and SHINNECOCK fetched up on the Norfolk Harbor Reach with the Naval Base off to port.

Next we boarded the docking pilot. With the harbor pilot's job complete, he finds his way into the chart room and the coffee mess. Meanwhile, the docking pilot starts his work, primarily directing the tugs to assist the ship into her berth. It appeared we would be berthing at Pier 20 in the "D and S," or Destroyer and Submarine, piers at the Norfolk Naval Station. I then heard a crackle on the radio; it was Borg's clearly distinguishable voice, "Stern...Bridge. Take a line from the tug through the Panama chock."

I acknowledged, "Bridge...Stern. Roger, take a line from the tug through the Panama chock." The *Panama chock* is the moniker for the centerline most chock on the transom, often referred to as the Panama chock due to the connection through such when in the Panama Canal. Shortly thereafter, the mooring detail on the stern took the line from the tug through the Panama chock and placed the eye over a set of bitts... the tugs now all made fast ready to work. I advised the men to stand clear of the line, as tug lines are known to part and take unsuspecting limbs with them.

It wasn't long after this the SHINNECOCK was made fast at Pier 20 Berth 6 starboard side holding *three two and two fore and aft*, "seamanese" for three headlines, two breast lines, and two spring lines forward and aft. Once the ship was secure and the mooring detail was dismissed, I heard the public address system notification, "In port watches will commence at 10:30." I knew I had the first in port day watch, which meant I would take over at 10:30 until 16:00.

At 10:30 I took the watch from Rob, as he was rip-roaring ready to go home. By the time I meandered down to the gangway area to check in with my "crack" watch team, the ship was a ghost town, for everyone who could depart for the day had already done so. Luckily for me, my "stellar" watch team of A/Bs Leter, Waddams, Stanz, and O/S Davis did not have time to go ashore to "tie one on" or, in the mariner vernacular, get drunk. I am certain that come 16:00 all four of these gents will be firmly seated at Nick's, the local watering hole.

The watch continued without incident until about 14:00, at which point my radio sounded off, "Mate on Watch...gangway. Please call the gangway."

As I was in the chartroom finishing some publication corrections, I answered, "Gangway...Mate on Watch. Roger." I slid off the chart table stool on which I was seated, walked to the chartroom door going to the bridge, gently opened the door, then pivoted and grabbed the ship's dial phone on the bulkhead behind the telemotor wheel.

Next A/B Leter picked up the phone, "Gangway... Leter..."

I interrupt him, "Leter... Mate on Watch. What's going on?"

A/B Leter stated, as if it were a common occurrence, "Mate, NIS is at the bottom of the gangway and they want to come aboard with the dogs."

My eyes opened wide and I blurted, "Tell them to remain at the foot of the gangway, do not allow them to board, and I will be right down."

I then hung up the phone. I proceeded to quietly walk to the starboard bridge wing; I poked my head over the rail and looked down. Sure enough there were what looked like a half a dozen agents and two German Shepherd dogs. As not to cause any undue panic, I ambled my way down to the gangway via the outside ladderwells, slowly and methodically touching on each step, with both hands on the railing.

I arrived at the gangway area, looked over to see not only A/B Leter, but also now Waddams and Stanz huddled around the gangway podium. I did not stop and say anything to them; rather I walked right past them, stepped off the ship onto the accommodation ladder, which is in use as the gangway, and continued down to the bottom. Upon arriving on the pier and seeing all the agents, I proclaimed, "Hi, I am the SHINNECOCK's Watch Officer, Frankie Natale. How may I help you?"

The lead agent stepped forward, presenting his badge and identification, then announced, "I am Special Agent Cooper with NIS. We are aware you just arrived back from deployment, and got a tip, so we are here to search for drugs."

I start thinking to myself, now what I am to do? I figured we might have drugs aboard; I know some people used them in the late night parties in Bill Reinhart's stateroom. Further, I thought, I can't allow these agents and their dogs aboard, it would certainly be the end for some of the crew and Captain Stone. His being a moron aside, I had to look out for him, right or wrong. He is my Captain. My mind made up, I put my hand up in a stop motion and declared, "I can't allow you to come aboard at this time as the Captain is off the ship and he needs to approve of any searches."

I must have hit a sensitive area with Special Agent Cooper for he forcefully retorted, "We are the Naval Investigative Service onboard the Naval Station and we demand to come aboard and conduct a search."

It must have been the fact I was so new and had no idea of the legalities and/or the rights of federal agents in regard to a federal ship and all, but I stood firm, "I am sorry, but I cannot allow you to come aboard at this time."

In saying this, I really had no authority or any possible way to stop them if they refused my order; nevertheless, Special Agent Cooper acquiesced, "OK, we will wait for the Captain."

With that, he handed me his card and asked that I pass it on to the Captain to call when he returns. I climbed back up the accommodation ladder to the ship, not quite knowing what had just happened, other than I stood fast for the ship. As it turned out later when the Old Man returned to the ship that evening and heard what transpired, I was his hero. Evidently, Captain Stone was regaling all the officers as to the David and Goliath story of me standing up to the NIS against an attempted unauthorized search. Unbeknownst to me at the time, NIS was attempting to conduct such an unlawful search. Moreover, NIS was banking on the fact the Captain and the senior officers would be ashore in the afternoon of arrival from deployment. They were further counting on an unsuspecting very junior officer remaining on duty, one whom they could easily bully to allow an illegitimate search.

It was 15:30 and I was sitting on the stool in the chartroom preparing for the end of my watch and the arrival of my relief who, luck would have it, was Matt. I knew he would relieve me a bit early as it was arrival homeport day and I hadn't been off the ship. In walked Matt early, as I had hoped, as he just returned from a few hours with his fiancé, who interestingly enough was my classmate back at Ft. Schuyler. Apparently, she drove down from Long Island and met the ship upon arrival this morning. As one may expect, Matt had a bit of a bounce in his step when he walked into the bridge and commented, "Hey Junior, how was the first watch in Norfolk?" Junior was a term of endearment with which he would address me from time to time, as I was the youngest of all the officers. Ironically, I was only two years younger than Matt, but I guess that's semantics. I proceeded to explain all the action corresponding to the incident with NIS, after which I conducted my in port turnover with Matt and, within ten minutes, finished.

Before departing the chartroom, I looked at Matt and asked, "What should I do now? Go to Nick's with everyone else?"

Matt shot back, "No, Nick's is for the unlicensed, and with so many there, it's almost like an unlicensed shipping hall. You go to Uncle Louie's. You can't walk there, like Nick's, so grab a cab—it's about a five minute ride. All the MSC officers hang out there when their ships are in port."

Curiously I replied, "Uncle Louie's it is then…I'll see you later," and I departed the chartroom to head down to my stateroom so as to get ready to go out. As I strode by the gangway podium on the way to my stateroom, I saw my watch team didn't even bother to change out of their uniforms; they were already walking down the pier after being relieved. I can only guess they were headed to Nick's.

I looked down on my watch, saw it was 18:00 and heard the voice, "That'll be $5.50." It was my taxi driver as we arrived outside Uncle Louie's Bar and Grill in the Ward's Corner section of Norfolk. All I had on me was a ten dollar bill and I wasn't about to bother with change, so I handed the cabbie the ten, opened the door, placed my feet firmly on the ground, and told him to keep the rest.

Uncle Louie's was a nice place. It was split into two sections, the restaurant section on one side and the lounge and bar on the other side. I opened the door and entered the lounge and I could see the bar on the right side. It was huge, and the place was immaculately clean with what seemed like new furnishings and a very upscale ambiance. This was certainly not like the bars in the Bronx when I was back at Ft. Schuyler. I later learned that in Virginia it was illegal to operate a dedicated bar; rather, all bars had to double as full restaurants, which would allow me to eat well and avoid bar fare type food. There were a handful of men sitting at the bar, and I peered at an empty seat. I wandered over, pulled the chair back and flung myself up on the seat. I said hello to the man on the left. Coincidentally, the fella would turn out to be my mentor, best friend, and confidant; however at this time, all I knew of him was his name, Jerry Ruprecht. He and I started to have a conversation, as it turned out he was the Chief Mate on another UNREP ship in port. His ship, the POLARIS, is unique in that she is a one hundred percent reefer ship, meaning all five cargo holds were either for frozen or refrigerated cargo. The POLARIS, also known as the "Queen of the Reefers," was further unique in that her UNREP gear was not of the STREAM type, like SHINNECOCK. Rather, POLARIS was old school pre-WWII in regard to UNREP, one of the last genuine "stick ships," as she utilized a modified Burton-rig with speed blocks for CONREP.

I took a liking to Jerry right away; clearly he was not in the mold of Captain Stone and his bootlicker bellyaching officers onboard the SHINNECOCK. No, Jerry was the genuine real deal, and without a doubt the Big Man upstairs was looking out for me by orchestrating this chance encounter. I remember my father telling me that if I find a dear friend to sail with, do so, as it will make the very hard life of going to sea all the more bearable. Jerry and I would go on to sail together for a total of fifteen years, most of which was with him as Captain and me as his Chief Mate.

Not knowing the layout, Jerry ordered me a "Depth Charge" cocktail, which was essentially a beer with a shot glass of, in this case, Jäger-meister liquor, dropped into the bottom of the beer glass. Before I knew it, a horde of MSC officers from other ships in port gathered around Jerry and me, joining in on the jubilations. We all ate and drank, and it was getting late, with last call being hailed, so we ordered our final drinks. The final drink bell rang, and I looked at my watch, it was an early 00:45—not even one in the morning. This was a world away from New York City and its last call was at five AM. Now the gaggle had dissipated to just three, Jerry, another ship's Chief Mate, Gino Brando from South Philly, and me. Jerry graciously paid the tab for everyone; he was known to be extremely generous, and my guess was he left a suitably large tip. Years later I would think this was odd, as Jerry was a Hollander from Michigan, and Hollanders are known to be not just frugal, but rather miserly. I would bet those Hollanders, like the Mainiacs, still had their First Communion money hidden away. However, Jerry must have been an anomaly, as he was more like the wise guys back in my neighborhood spreading around the "moolah."

We walked out of Uncle Louie's and right to Jerry's new BMW sedan. We were all nicely inebriated, but these were different times, and we loaded into Jerry's car. At this point, I went to grab the front passenger door, but I was pushed aside as Gino Brando, thoroughly liquored up as well, demanded he ride "shotgun." He commanded, in his best-slurred speech, "I am a Chief Mate and you are just a Third Mate… you sit in the back."

I attempted to plead my case, "You probably want me to ride in the front; I get carsick in the back."

Bravo shot back, "Yeah, well, deal with it," and then he slid into the seat and closed the door.

Reluctantly, with no other choice, I climbed into the very cramped back seat, for this was no "land yacht" of a car. Jerry took off and seemed to be doing quite well; I can only assume he'd made the trek from Uncle Louie's to the ship a few times, to say the least.

Within five minutes, I start to feel the nausea, and it's hitting me like a ton of bricks. I went to lower the window so as to stick my head out, and wouldn't you guess, it's one of those child safety windows that only opens a crack. Uh oh, I started to panic, I can't stop it and with that, I projectile vomited all over the back of the passenger seat, the back door, and the rear window. Gino Brando starts berating me with something to the effect of "what kind of mariner can I be if I cannot hold my liquor."

I think, what an imbecile, I had no problem holding my liquor, it was sitting in the back seat which caused me to "refund" my drinks. Unbelievably, Jerry did not mutter much of anything for me just soiling his new car. Nope…he did not degrade me, shame me, or cajole me… nothing, except to say, "We better get you something to eat." Of course, eating was the last thing on my mind, as I was so queasy. I just wanted to put my forehead on something cool.

The next thing I know, I look up and Jerry is pulling into a 7-11 convenience store. He and Gino Brando exit the car and proceed into the store. I can only assume they were going to get me something to eat and maybe something for themselves. I couldn't take it anymore, even though the car was parked, everything was spinning, and I still needed something cold on my head. I opened the back door of the BMW, gingerly stepped out, as I know I am impaired, and stood for a second. As I started to sway back and forth, I started to lie down in the empty parking space next to the BWM. Now I am fully supine in the middle of the parking space and the cool concrete feels great against my forehead. But wouldn't you know it, a car pulls in, and lucky for me, they see me spread eagle in the space and thankfully do not run me over. Seeing the car bumper mere inches from my head, I attempted to rise to a standing position. Once upright, I failed to remember that Jerry and Gino Brando remained inside the 7-11 and further, I don't even recognize the BMW from which I just exited. With that, I started walking, or at least putting one foot in front of the other, while trying to remain erect. Seeing the entrance to the Navy Base across busy Hampton Boulevard, I headed in that direction. I must have been quite a sight, falling down drunk, venturing back down a divided highway in early hours of the morning. A car pulled up beside me, a window was lowered, and I heard a voice, "Sir, are you OK?"

I shot back, "I'm fine. Leave me alone. I'm from New York," like that meant anything to these Good Samaritans just looking out for a drunken mariner. The window closed and the car drove off. I somehow crossed the gauntlet of speeding cars and big rigs that is Hampton Boulevard and walked past the gate guard. I had the wherewithal to actually remove my mariner ID card and present it as I continued past the guard. Evidently, I, along with my condition of intoxication, must have appeared normal, as the gate guard just waved me through. Moreover, this was long before the stringent security enhancements post the September 11th, 2001 terrorist attacks.

The next thing I know, I find my way all the way to Pier 20, most astonishing due to the fact this was the first time I had been off the ship and at the Norfolk Naval Station, and yet was still able to navigate myself back to the ship. I found the gangway and started climbing the ladder. When I reached the top, I stopped and started to sway, not unlike the little Chief Engineer Nowak back in Rodman. However, I did not fall back, I pressed forward with purpose, passed Cargo Mate

LAS at the gangway, and headed to my stateroom. As I was trudging off, I heard LAS exclaim, "Whoa, he's loaded..."

When I reached my stateroom, I realized I was rather drunk, so I figured that I needed to drink water to flush my system. I opened my fridge and grabbed a gallon bottle of water and started chugging. Half the water went in my mouth; the other half spilled down my neck and all over my clothes. Next, I felt very warm, so I stripped down to my boxers and undershirt. I believe I needed to walk it off, so I departed my stateroom, went out the watertight door to the UNREP deck and started trying to walk off the intoxication. After a few minutes, and realizing through my stupor that this was not working, I headed back to my stateroom. I opened the door and thought to myself, I need to eat something. I looked over on my desk and saw a bag of Rold Gold pretzels; I snatched them up, took my two hands and ripped the bag open, causing pretzels to fly all over the room, my rack, and me. I looked up, feeling rather dizzy, turned and collapsed right on my rack, staring at the bright overhead lights—and passed out.

I opened my eyes and who did I see staring at me? None other than Captain Stone, Second Mate Matt, and Cargo Mate LAS, and I heard Stone remark, "He's alive. It looks like he's OK."

In the passageway, I heard garbled mouth Borg add, "I guess he's a mariner now."

I sit up and Captain Stone was laughing in a deep bellowing howl, as he exited my stateroom; LAS chuckled in unison with his mentor as he also departed, and Matt looked at me, and commented, "You must have had quite a night. Get up, you've got the watch at 08:00..."

As Matt exited my stateroom I thought, another day on SHINNECOCK...

EPILOGUE

"The superior mariner will use his superior knowledge to avoid situations requiring the use of his superior skill..."

- CAPT Sean P. Tortora

Master Mariner

Circa 2009

I finally made it to Djibouti, albeit a dozen years and twenty or so ships later. However, when I arrived, I was the Captain of the ship, an UNREP ship. By way of explanation, officially called the Republic of Djibouti, pronounced "Jih-BOO-tee," is a city state located in East Africa at the Horn of Africa formed by the Red Sea and the Gulf of Aden to the east, bordered by Somalia to the south, Ethiopia to the west, and Eritrea to the north. Djibouti was a French colony until its independence in 1977 and, as such, much of the port was designed and engineered by the French Foreign Legion, but more on that later. Djibouti is strategically located near one of the world's busiest shipping lanes, including critical maritime chokepoints such as the Bab El Mandeb Straits in an area of heavy pirate activity. As such, it developed into a vital U.S. Navy logistic hub, complete with the U.S. Marine Corps base Camp Lemonier, or "Camp Lemonade" as commonly referred to by the mariners. Hence the reason I was required to…Steam to Djibouti.

Now Djibouti is the most unique place to which my travels have ever taken me. I mean that in the most disturbing manner. To say Djibouti is a depressed destination is indeed an understatement. I have often said, "The city of Djibouti in the country of Djibouti is so nice, they named it twice." This phrase was always succeeded by the description, "If the world ever needed an enema, Djibouti would be the insertion point." Astonishingly, Djibouti is home to a five-star international hotel and resort, The Kempinski. I often referred to it as an oasis of luxury and excess surrounded by abject poverty and hardship. This is being kind, for the Kempinski's very own brochure describes Djibouti as "a disturbing but fascinating experience." Outside of the hotel's heavily armed and walled property exists a country racked by governmental strife and corruption. However, so strategically located is Djibouti, that they are also well aware of their geopolitical and forward-deployed logistic significance to other nations…most certainly the U.S. The nefarious Djiboutian leaders, knowing they hold the winning hand, negotiate port and base access with their own best interests in mind, and not those of their citizens. Most people live in make-shift huts composed of trash and debris scavenged from the port. They barely have enough food and water, and certainly have no plumbing, indoor or otherwise. Notwithstanding, the unscrupulous leaders have devised a plan to keep the masses befuddled. The Djiboutian government provides a daily dose of *Khat* promptly at 13:00. Khat is a plant native to the Horn of Africa which produces a hallucinogenic effect with side effects of euphoria and loss of appetite —the perfect remedy for the ails of the people's wretched existence. In essence, Djibouti keeps their rank and file all hopped up on drugs.

As Captain, from the minute we took arrival until the ship was moored, I was required to be ever vigilant with pinpoint focus more so than in any other port. This was due primarily to the lack of competent harbor pilots, ship-assist tug operators and poor harbor control communicators. The French Foreign Legion, as I previously mentioned, designed the port itself, and a mariner has to wonder what in God's creation were they thinking. On one side of the port was the cargo pier and on the other side sat the cargo fuel pier. Unfortunately, in order for a deep draft vessel, such as an UNREP ship, to shift from one pier to the other, it actually required such a ship to exit the port, steam eleven miles around and then reenter the port at the other service pier. Interestingly enough, the actual solid cargo and cargo fuel piers were only two and a half miles apart if steamed directly. Sadly, that would require the ship to transit a "land bridge" as there was a rather large shoal with an eight meter or twenty-six feet three-inch depth, way too shallow for a large UNREP ship to steam across. One would only question the French Foreign Legion's thinking in regard to dredging, or lack thereof.

A normal resupply for the fleet at Djibouti for my UNREP ship required a solid cargo load out of approximately seven hundred lifts of stores, munitions, and perishables, and then a cargo fuel lift of several million gallons of both diesel marine fuel and jet fuel. This also must be accomplished within thirty-six hours over the course of one overnight port stay.

The first part of the resupply was always the solid cargo load out. This was due to the fact the ship was lighter, or drew less draft, after servicing the fleet all week, coupled with the solid cargo pier controlling depth of only ten and half meters. Whereas the cargo fuel pier depth averaged twenty and half meters. The ship draft, when *full and down,* meaning fully loaded and down to its marks, was approximately twelve meters, thus dictating our load out for fleet resupply.

Upon taking arrival at the port of Djibouti, as mentioned, I would steam the ship to the southeastern cargo side of the port. Prior to entering, as Captain, I have the ship's navigator, the Second Mate, hold an intensive pre-arrival navigation brief for all personnel involved with operations. I should mention a pre-arrival navigation brief is required as per international seagoing law, and most of these briefs are quite routine. However, not so when arriving in Djibouti, as special attention must be given to the ship's interface with both the harbor pilot and the tugs, due to their qualifications and skills (or lack thereof), as they are suspect. In addition, Djibouti does not employ docking pilots. A senior Port Captain once facetiously commented the Djiboutian pilots' training includes safely conning bicycles down the pier, then moving right up to piloting Navy ships. Joking aside, Djibouti was corrupt and the pilots were most certainly appointed to their positions due to their family standing in the regime.

On this particular day when bringing my ship into the port, the tugs and pilot were late, which I would learn is standard operating procedure. To make matters a bit more precarious, there is a point upon entering the port of Djibouti which I refer to as the "point of no return." The exact position is in the vicinity of Buoy number 2, which not coincidentally is also the pilot pick-up point as well. Essentially, Buoy 2 is at the cusp of the convergence of two entrance channels combined with the adjacent designated anchorage. When crossing such, there is no way to turn the vessel around without the assistance of tugs. Further, the channel ends with a substantial shoal in a mere one and a quarter miles, thus necessitating the need to make the turn, with tug assistance, so as to come alongside the very last berth before reaching the shoal. Due to force protection considerations, MSC ships always dock at berth number ten, or Fontainebleau Point, which is the very last berth with sufficient water under the keel. As such, it is at Buoy 2; there is no way out.

Out of abundance of safety, especially in this port, I prefer to have the pilot onboard and the two tugs standing by to assist when arriving at Buoy 2, that critical point in the channel. On this, my first occasion steaming to Djibouti, I would not have that luxury. The Second Mate transmitted over the VHF radio, "Djibouti Port Control…Djibouti Port Control…Djibouti Port Control…this is USNS MASSAPEQUA on channel thirteen…Over…"

Port Control responded, "USNS MASSAPEQUA...Djibouti Port Control...Roger...Over..."

With my direction the Second Mate continued, "Djibouti Port Control, this is MASSAPEQUA. We are abeam Buoy 2, standing by for pilot and tugs and entering the channel. We do not see the pilot boat or tugs... Over..."

Port Control nonchalantly retorted, "MASSAPEQUA, Yes, Yes, Yes, Pilot and tugs coming. Port Control Out..."

And with that, I proceeded on, as we had a hard timetable to keep and I knew the pilot and tugs would be arriving shortly. Although I proceeded, it was with great caution, having both anchors ready to let go if needed, and the engines standing by for immediate maneuver. I was ready for any contingency. Sure enough, the pilot boat appeared almost immediately after I completed my first turn around Huron Shoals into the poorly buoyed channel. I could see the two tugs in the distance heading my way.

Not soon after, the escorted pilot arrived on the bridge. He was clearly of North African or Middle Eastern descent, swarthy and ruddy, middle-aged, very short in stature, maybe five-foot tall, and a bit heavy around the middle. The pilot sported short-cropped hair, dressed in a rather unkempt manner, and emitted an almost unbearably offensive body odor. When he opened his mouth to speak, it was apparent oral hygiene is not top on his list, as he had maybe five teeth remaining in his head—and those were putrid. To my surprise, accompanying my Lilliputian pilot was a young man in similar dress and bouquet of maybe fifteen or sixteen. I didn't ask but I assumed it was his son training to be a pilot himself.

When the pilot and I conducted our turnover in his best-broken English, I had both engines rung up at DEAD SLOW AHEAD on the EOT. Recall, the Captain never relinquishes Command of the vessel to the pilot, and the pilot is only a hired "local expert" on the port and ability to work with the tugs. However, the Captain does permit the pilot to conn the vessel into the port. A competent Captain will oversee the pilot like a hawk, ready to jump in and make corrections if necessary, not like Captain Stone on SHINNECOCK, who would often nap in his chair when the pilot was conning.

The pilot and I walked out the starboard bridge wing and he ordered FULL AHEAD on both engines. I instantly questioned the pilot as to such an order with the channel's rather short length, the shoaling dead ahead, and finally the need to make up the tugs and pivot the vessel around to land on the pier starboard side-to. He began mumbling incoherently, so I walked into the bridge and told the Third Mate to ring up SLOW AHEAD on the EOT for both engines, and then I walked back out on the starboard bridge wing. The pilot was none the wiser, and I knew from this time forward, I may have to countermand every order going forward. I was thinking to myself, had I not reduced the speed immediately, we would have certainly run this ship hard aground. Unfortunately, the "keystone cops-like pilot and tugs show" was just beginning.

The pilot called in one tug to make up to our port side midship. All of a sudden the entire ship swayed. The tug came in at a high speed and rammed the MASSAPEQUA on the perpendicular. The tug's bow slammed into the midship of the hull so hard and with so much force that she shuddered the fifty-thousand-ton ship. Calling the tug to ascertain what happened and listening to the tug operator on the radio, it occurred to me, the tug crew was all hopped up on the free Khat the government provides its minions. They were truly smoking dope while working with my ship! When I questioned the pilot, his answer, "Captain…OK …OK…nothing wrong." Yeah right—nothing wrong. I had the Chief Mate call the Bosun to take a look and see what, if anything, took place on the hull. As it turned out the Bosun could not see much, but he did think the hull was dented. Now my mental safety radar sounded, for the tug may have holed the skin of the ship; this would have a definite effect on the mission, as I could not take the ship to sea with a hole in the watertight hull. The only positive was the fact that the ship was a double hull and if indeed the tug did hole the ship, the oil would not spill. But this was not the time or the place to contemplate the "what ifs;" I had to finish safely mooring the ship with this buffoon of a pilot and tug operators.

Clearly it became more and more apparent I would have to relieve the pilot of his duties as he was destined to either run the ship aground or damage her. At this time both tugs were securely made fast to the ship, so I did not have the need for the pilot to provide direction. I turned to the pilot and relayed, "OK, Mr. Pilot. Thank you. I'll take it from here." Immediately, he started jumping up and own and blurted out, "I am Captain now. I am in charge." Meanwhile, as he was jumping and his arms were flailing, his son was chiming in, yelping to his father, "You say...you Captain...this US Navy ship...You say...you boss...you say... U.S. follow your orders."

I could only assume in the corrupt Djiboutian caste-type system, that the pilot who brings in a U.S. Navy ship is the highest caste. Further, I speculated that these pilots do, in fact, believe that they actually take over the command of a U.S. Navy ship when they are onboard. But alas, I had the safety of the ship to consider and neither the time nor the patience to contemplate the situation. I leaned over and spoke into the Chief Mate's ear, "Call the ship's store operator, tell him to bring up shirts, lighters, and hats...tell him I will settle up with him later." In the interim, my Hobbit-like pilot continued to proclaim he was the Captain of my ship and I must relinquish Command and control to him. Adding to this was the pilot's son, who was now in tears because he believed his father lied to him about taking over the big U.S. Navy ship. While I was conning the ship through the turn at the terminus of the channel heading to our berth, the pilot was jumping and screaming, the son was wailing with gnashing of teeth. I continued to ignore the fit and conniption acted out on the bridge wing before me.

The ship's store operator arrived on the bridge with all his tchotchkes and handed them over to me. I instantly turned around and offered them to the pilot and his son while saying, "Mr. Pilot, to thank you for all your help, I would like to give you these." All of a sudden, the pilot stopped flailing and the son ceased blubbering, and an eerie calm came about. The pilot was now smiling and so happy. He and his son were looking at all the goodies as if it were Christmas morning opening presents. In his exuberance with his haul of baksheesh, the pilot had totally abandoned his obstinacy and huddled in the corner of the bridge, examining his goodies. Satisfied with my de-escalation and handling of the situation, I asked the Chief Mate to occupy our "guests" and make sure they got off the ship safely once we were secured alongside.

I brought the ship alongside and we commenced mooring. Once we had the first line across and were resting smartly against the pier, I turned over the tying up to the Chief Mate and said, "Mr. Mate, you can take it from here. Please make her up, three, two, and two fore and aft and put out the CT wires as springs midship. I have to go down and meet with the Navy liaison and ship's agent. Oh, and there is that little item about a possible dent or hole in the hull I need to deal with…"

The Chief Mate complied, "Roger Captain…let me know if you need anything else." As I departed the starboard bridge wing, where my pilot and his son continued to be engrossed with their treasures waiting to go ashore, the Chief Mate hollered back to me, "Captain… you gotta see this…"

I was just about to enter the bridge proper from the wing, but I turned and dashed over to the end of the bridge wing next to the Chief Mate. I looked forward at the headline; I even took my binoculars out of my chair caddy, brought them to my eyes, and couldn't believe what I was witnessing. I had to remove the binoculars, rub my eyes, and then place them back up, and look again. To my utter dismay, there appeared to be two Djiboutians squatting on the headlines like a perch over the water commencing the act of defecating. Making matters worse, in the rancid polluted harbor waters just below these men, several other people were what appeared to be bathing.

The walkie-talkie radio then crackled, "Bridge. This is bow. Over…"

The Chief Mate responded, "Bow, this the bridge. Go ahead…"

The Cargo Mate on the bow continued, "Bridge, are you seeing this? The two guys on the headlines? My crew down here doesn't want to touch the lines now. We need to heave around this line. What do you want me to do?…"

The Chief Mate looked at me for guidance. I passed on that we should get a bleach water solution and as the line is hauled aboard have one A/B day worker on the bow use a long-handled scrub brush on the line. And, when finished, to make certain to flush the mooring line with fresh water so as not to allow the bleach to destroy the line. In the end, my makeshift decontamination protocol provided the needed safety to the crew and they were able to complete the mooring process.

As it turned out, the tug with the operators zonked out on Khat did indeed put a hole in the hull. Thankfully the hole was above the water-line and only in the outer shell of the double hull. However, this required a repair and regulatory body inspection prior to getting underway. This meant the MASSAPEQUA would rest alongside the cargo pier for two days. Of course, this affected our follow on commitments for UNREP and resupplying the fleet; most notably, the aircraft carrier would now have to wait, and that is not optimal. Luckily, the fleet was well aware of the challenges when…steaming to Djibouti…

ABOUT THE AUTHOR

CAPT Sean P. Tortora, MS, USMS is a Master Mariner with twenty-five years at sea. He is also an unlimited Master of towing vessels and Master of underway replenishment vessels. During his career at sea, CAPT Tortora has had Command of many different vessels including tankers, general cargo, break bulk, ammunition, ocean towing and salvage, special mission, as well as underway replenishment vessels. CAPT Tortora has conducted over 2,000 underway replenishment evolutions during his career.

CAPT Tortora is native on Long Island, New York, and is a graduate of Chaminade High School and holds both a Master's and a Bachelor's degree from the State University of New York Maritime College at Ft. Schuyler. He has served in the first Gulf War – Operation Desert Storm/Desert Sortie 1991-1992, Operation Noble Eagle – the response to the September 11, 2001 terrorist attacks on the World Trade Center, and the second Gulf War – Operation Iraqi Freedom 2002-2010. After retiring from the sea, CAPT Tortora is now an Associate Professor in the Department of Marine Transportation at the United States Merchant Marine Academy at Kings Point, New York.

CAPT Tortora is the author of the marine firefighting textbook, *Study Guide for Marine Fire Prevention, Firefighting, and Fire Safety,* published by Cornell Maritime Press. Read more about CAPT Tortora at LongIslandMaritime.com

CPSIA information can be obtained
at www.ICGtesting.com
Printed in the USA
LVHW081014050321
680213LV00010B/21

9 781952 859625